The Long Crossing

*William Ratigan's Great Lakes Panorama**

SOO CANAL!

YOUNG MISTER BIG

HIAWATHA AND AMERICA'S MIGHTIEST MILE

STRAITS OF MACKINAC!

THE ADVENTURES OF CAPTAIN MC CARGO

THE LONG CROSSING

HIGHWAYS OVER BROAD WATERS

THE BLUE SNOW

THE ADVENTURES OF PAUL BUNYAN & BABE

TINY TIM PINE

* See page 149 and following pages.

THE
LONG
CROSSING

BY

WILLIAM RATIGAN

Illustrated by Dick Rienstra

William B. Eerdmans, Grand Rapids, Michigan

Contents

THE LONG CROSSING

Where voyageurs once made **Le Grand Traverse**
Vacationers now make the Long Crossing
On singing wheels that navigate the Straits
An eagle flight above the ghost canoes
Riding the rainbowed mist.

Across the ages and in every clime
Where man has blazed a trail of high adventure
To challenge distant shores in thought or space,
All men have shared the joy of the Long Crossing,
Riding the rainbowed dream.

W.R.

One

School Reporter at the Straits

And the biggest bridge you ever saw
Is at the Straits of Mackinac!
—Watchman's Ditty

SUNNING HIMSELF in the captain's chair at the Lower Peninsula approach to the world's greatest suspension span, the Watchman on Mackinac Bridge thoughtfully stuffed his long Irish clay pipe with a cigar that Michigan's Governor Williams had handed him months agone.

Puffing like a steamboat headed upstream, the one-time sailing master, whose deep-water blue eyes had learned to measure the worth of men and boats by the cut of their jibs, squinted at the young fellow in the school jacket who had introduced himself and stated his business with a glad-to-meet-you voice that went in keeping with his hearty handshake and his catching smile. The boy had a straightforward entry, too — no blundering off on the wrong tack or backing water; he sailed right to the point. To be sure, he seemed able to ask more questions in ten minutes than a college professor could answer in ten years, but that was a favorable sign. People who asked silly questions deserved to get silly answers, but people who never asked questions at all might as well phone the undertaker; they were dead, only they didn't know it.

The weathered old Great Lakes sailor tilted back his

9

skipper cap, a sure signal that the wind of his somewhat cantankerous nature blew in the right direction toward the boy. "So you're a reporter on your school paper and you want to write a story about the Long Crossing. First, let me ask you a couple of questions. Why did you pick me to interview for all the information?"

"I read about you in the newspapers, sir, and in the book that told about you walking across the bridge even before it was entirely built. I guess there were places where you had to be like a tight-rope walker at the circus."

The veteran sailing master nodded, matter-of-factly. "I had some good training behind me, son. After you climb enough masts on troubled water, with the wind playing crack-the-whip to throw you overboard, you get to have eyes in the bottom of your feet and you learn to hang on by the skin of your teeth."

"But you did walk across the bridge and back before it was all finished?" The young man unpocketed a workmanlike notebook and pencil. "Excuse me for asking, sir, but a reporter has to make sure of his facts. What the book said, that was all real, wasn't it?"

"As real as anything." The Watchman on Mackinac Bridge winked broadly. "Of course, son, you got to take what these writers say with a grain of salt. The best of them are Irish, and no Irishman ever let the truth interfere with the telling of a good story. But, as Captain McCargo of the schooner *Minong* used to say: 'What is truth but an Irish fable?' "

Two

Lake Algonquin and the Killarney Mountains

Made a passage safe and certain,
Made a pathway for the people.
Song of Hiawatha

ACCORDING TO WHAT the Lakeman told the School Reporter, an Indian fable was an early part of the Mackinac Bridge story. In fact, even going back into the past millions of years, there were Irish and Indian names used to describe the great changes on the earth's surface that had led to the creation of the Straits of Mackinac, and consequently the need for a bridge.

The Watchman's many friends on the Lake Survey boats — geologists and botanists and zoologists from the universities of Michigan and Illinois and Wisconsin and Minnesota — professors who tested temperatures and could see whole worlds of plants and animals in a drop of lake water under a microscope — sailors with fancy college degrees, who sank tubes deep into the lake beds and brought up long cores of prehistoric sediment from which they could figure, by examining the different folds and layers and levels, the life story of the Lake, the same way a tree's age can be counted by the rings in the trunk — these fresh-water oceanographers had taught the veteran skipper that there had been a time lasting hundreds of millions of years when great seas invaded much of the continents of North America.

11

During this period untold tons of salt and lime were deposited in the basins carved out by these prehistoric oceans, a process which set the stage for the Midland brine wells that supplied modern chemical plants and for the Upper Lakes stone quarries that supplied the 600 thousand barrels of cement and 440 thousand cubic yards of concrete used in the construction of the 32 water piers of the Long Crossing.

This was a staggering thought to both the old Lakes captain and the young School Reporter — that it had taken hundreds of millions of years for nature to furnish the materials that went into the making of Mackinac Bridge. It seemed almost beyond belief that the longest suspension span in history had been made possible by countless billions and trillions of tiny forms of shell life swarming in the tropical seas which once rolled across Middle America as primitive ancestors of Moby Dick showed their armor-plated flukes and spouted geysers of salt water from Ontario to Ohio.

All this might be hard to believe, but, if any Doubting Thomas from Missouri happened along who had to be shown, the evidence could be seen and picked up along the beaches of Lake Michigan and Lake Huron where fossilized stones were constantly washed ashore from coral reefs formed when the North Country lay under the spell of the tropics. Known as Petoskey stones on the Lake Michigan bend of the Straits of Mackinac and as Alpena stones around the Lake Huron bend, these fragments of early life from the dawn of the world could be cut and polished into articles of costume jewelry.

Watchman (rocking on the back legs of the captain's chair): Takes all kinds to make a world, doesn't it, son? Give two men the same materials, and one of them builds the greatest bridge on earth and the other makes a belt ornament or a pair of earrings.

Reporter (grinning as he makes a note) : *Belt-buckle or bridge?*

The Watchman on Mackinac Bridge gave a matching grin and went on with the rest of the story. Between a billion and two billion years ago, he explained, while most of Michigan and the Upper Great Lakes region was still drowned by the tropical seas, the surface of the world globe, as it had been doing for ages, went on cooling and shrinking. During this process huge wrinkles were formed in the earth's crust, and these wrinkles became mountain ranges, even larger than the Rocky Mountains of today's western states. One of these ranges that rose high above the surrounding water has been named after the lake region of Ireland and is called by geologists the Killarney Mountains.

Millions of years passed away, and slowly the Killarney Mountains that ran across Minnesota and Wisconsin and the Upper Peninsula of Michigan were worn down by frost and sunshine, and wind and ice, and running water. Streams and rivers, cascading down the slopes of the Killarney Mountains carried away layer after layer of lighter rock until only the heavier ore-carrying rocks remained. Pockets of huge iron deposits and masses of pure copper bigger than houses were exposed near the surface from Ishpeming to Isle Royale as the Killarney Range that once had boasted summits higher than Pike's Peak was weathered down to stumps that might be called the sawed-off Rocky Mountains. These stumps or *roots* of the great Killarney chain, known in Michigan as the Huron and the Porcupine Mountains, are seen today in the old lava flows of the Keweenaw Peninsula and in ore outcroppings around Iron Mountain.

The tropical seas and the Killarney Mountains ruled

the Upper Great Lakes region at least 450 million years ago, a fact that made the Watchman on Mackinac Bridge and the young School Reporter shake their heads in wondering awe. It was all very well for geologists, men who could go down a mine shaft or look at a cliff-side and read layers of rock as easily as the average person thumbed the pages of a book, to take such long periods of time for granted, but it made the sailor with his pipe and the boy with his note-pad catch their breath.

To any geologist, the glacial period that finally formed the Great Lakes into the region recognized on modern maps took place only a mere matter of a million years ago, which to the experts is no more than yester-day in geological times. During this so-called "recent" event, vast sheets of ice in the form of glaciers gathered in the snowfields of Canada and slowly spread over the surface of the northern half of the North American con-tinent, covering its surface with a blanket of ice that, according to Professor Bergquist of Michigan State University, was probably a mile or more in thickness. As he remarked on this, the Watchman on Mackinac Bridge asked the School Reporter:

"How'd you like to go fishing through *that* ice, son? You'd have to wait around all morning before your sinker hit bottom!"

One of these glaciers of a million years ago came down from Hudson Bay, the ice advancing sixteen hundred miles almost to the present Ohio River. It was this mass of ice that spread over Michigan in sev-eral invasions and shaped the hills and valleys and plains and placed the rivers and lakes almost as they are located today. And it was the melting water from this ice that collected in basins to form the Great Lakes.

The first of the glacial invasions pushed down from Canada at about the time that the Ape-man of Java came upon the earth.

Watchman (cheerfully): He's got a regular official title, son, but I can't pronounce it or spell it, neither.

Reporter (scribbling with pride): *Pithecanthropus erectus,* sir.

The last invasion of the ice sheet from the refrigerator box up near Hudson Bay came to an end about the time that Cromagnon civilization was spreading in Europe. In other words, it is a good guess that the retreating glacier left the Lake Superior basin some ten thousand years ago.

Michigan was right in the center of all the glacial activity, which accounts for the fact that it borders upon four of the five Great Lakes. As the last glacier crunched slowly south, scouring the old tropical sea bottoms and bulldozing mountains of rock from one place to another, there were huge troughs sculptured out. In this way, after modifying the pre-glacial valleys into basins, the retreat of the ice allowed the water to pond. As the lobes or tongues of ice at the front of the glacier melted, little lakes started to form in the basins, and the more the ice melted the larger the lakes became.

Finally, after ten thousand years, all these lakes left behind by the melted glacier flowed together in one great body of water, Lake Algonquin.

Watchman: There's the Indian name to match your Irish Killarney, son!

Lake Algonquin, still bordered by the glacier along its northern shore, was born when the sheet of ice, at least as wide as three states and as deep as a mile, had entirely melted from the Great Lakes region. It was at this time that the Straits of Mackinac first appeared, forming a spillway through a glacial gorge to connect the overflowing waters in the Superior, Huron, and Michigan basins.

Four thousand years passed, in what geologists would call the twinkling of an eye. Then, about six thousand years ago, while the pyramids were being built in Egypt, and when the margin of the ice sheet retreated across a low point in the divide at North Bay, Ontario, the lake water of the Huron and Michigan basins was drained down — Huron to about 400 feet below its present level and Michigan to 350 feet below present level. This was the Lake Chippewa stage in the formation of the Great Lakes, so named by the Watchman's good friend Jack I. Hough, Professor of Geology at the University of Illinois.

Lake Chippewa drained through the Straits of Mackinac in a steep-sided canyon seventy miles long. Then, with the enormous weight of ice removed, the North Country tilted up, as if a great trap door had been opened, and this raised the outlet channel at North Bay so the lake level rose back up to the old Algonquin level again to form the five Great Lakes and their connecting waters into the St. Lawrence Seaway, almost as shown on a modern map.

As the change in climate led to good hunting and fishing, an Indian people, made up of several tribes including the Ottawas and the Chippewas (called Ojibways by Longfellow in the "Song of Hiawatha"), came to settle along the shores of the Upper Great Lakes, and particularly near the two historic crossings, the Straits of Mackinac and the other water barrier fifty miles farther north between the American and the Canadian Soo.

These Indian tribes formed the Algonquin nation, and the idea of both a bridge at the Straits and a canal

at the Soo went deep into their folklore. Around Algonquin campfires in the misty past, when the pipe of
peace, the calumet, went from hand to hand, the old
chiefs told the story of Hiawatha who had been sent
among the Ottawas and the Chippewas to clear their
rivers, forests, and fishing grounds — *to make a passage
for the people, make a pathway safe and certain.*

After clearing a safe channel from Sault Ste. Marie
so that Lake Superior could be connected with the
Lower Lakes, the fabled Algonquin engineer came to
the Straits of Mackinac and constructed a crossing with
a bridge of stones picked up along the shore. According
to the legend a great storm destroyed the bridge but
remnants survive in what are now known as Bois Blanc,
Round, and Mackinac Islands.

It was a strange and wonderful tale that geology told,
a tale of tropical seas and tiny coral animals and seventy-
five foot icthyosauri with eyes as large as dinner plates,
a tale of invading glaciers and tongues of ice melting
into five of the world's greatest lakes, a tale of tremendous changes in the earth's surface, caused by forces far
more powerful than man-made atom bombs.

Perhaps the most wonderful part of the story was that
these same forces and changes that had created the need
for a bridge at the Straits of Mackinac also had created
the materials to build the bridge, and created them
hundreds of millions of years in advance.

Watchman: There's Nature's planning for you, son!

The Killarney Mountains had stored up the iron ore
in the Lake Superior region, the iron that went from
Duluth and Marquette through the Soo Canal and
down the old Huron and Michigan arms of Lake Algonquin to be made into steel at Chicago and Gary and
Cleveland and Pittsburgh, the steel that came back up

the Lakes in the form of girders and dinosaur-skeleton sections to be fitted into a total length of 19,243 feet that formed the superstructure of the Long Crossing.

Through the ages the Killarney Mountains also had stored up the copper ore on the Keweenaw Peninsula and on Isle Royale and at White Pine, copper that was smelted into ingots and then given a round-trip ticket down the Lakes to be converted into wires and conduits so the Long Crossing could be lighted up at night, copper that had melted and fused together deep inside the Killarney Mountains perhaps a billion years before the Straits of Mackinac had been opened by the surging waters of Lake Algonquin.

Watchman: Look out across the Straits, son. See the white line that goes around the top of Mackinac Island like a hatband along where the guns of the old British fort used to scowl at the French and at Chief Pontiac and at our own Mad Anthony Wayne and Commodore Perry? That line marks the old Lake Algonquin beachhead. Back in the days when the Big Lake started carving a passage through the Straits by way of a glacial canyon, you could have waded out into the water from up there. Now you'd have to take a high dive of more than eight hundred feet off the cliff before you made a belly-splash.

Reporter (scribbling furiously) : I don't see why they call the Mississippi the Father of Waters. I'd pick Lake Algonquin — the Father of the Great Lakes!

Watchman: Spoken like a Michigander, son. And if any state officials are eavesdropping, you'll probably be made an honorary Michigan Commodore and Admiral of the Inland Seas.

Mention of the Inland Seas reminded the old sailor and the young reporter of the rolling tropical seas that once had washed across the Great Lakes region, the oceans alive with fish whose tiny bones and shells had formed the huge limestone deposits at Petoskey and Alpena and Rogers City and Calcite, the limestone that not only had figured in the hundreds of thousands of tons of cement and concrete poured to form the piers and anchorages of the Long Crossing, but the limestone that also had been used in smelting the iron ore in the Killarney Mountains into the steel now framing the bridge. Only ninety miles below the Straits of Mackinac, as if put there on purpose to help build the Mackinac Bridge, was located the largest limestone quarry in the world, formed during the Devonian period 350 million years ago in the Paleozoic era on the Huron glacial tongue of old Lake Algonquin.

Reporter (spelling under his breath slowly as he writes) : P-a-l-e-o-z-o-i-c. A-l-g-o-n-q-u-i-n.

Watchman (puffing his long clay pipe): So there you are, son. No matter how far back into history you go, you can't get ahead of the Irish and the Indians, not with the Killarney Mountains and Lake Algonquin on deck. And, just to round out this part of the Mackinac Bridge story and bring it up to now, the engineer who designed the bridge and had charge of building it was an honorary Indian of six tribes with the title of Great Chief Who Walks Across Great Rivers On Iron, but he must have been an adopted Irishman too because when he started the new fashion of painting bridges bright instead of black or battleship gray, he never made any fuss about any particular color — as long as it turned out to be some shade of green!

Reporter (wonderingly): That's right. Except for the ivory towers, the whole rest of the bridge is painted green!

Watchman (chuckling) : Sure and begorrah, me lad, and haven't I been after telling you that all the steel came from Killarney?

Three

Crossroads of the Great Lakes

Who passed this way one yesterday?
Ten voyageurs with Pere Marquette.
Ten thousand ghost canoes and phantom sails
are passing yet.
                          Straits of Mackinac!

SO AS NOT TO SHOW any favoritism in his brand of politics, the Watchman on Mackinac Bridge stuffed his pipe the second time with a cigar given to him during the Mackinac Bridge dedication by Secretary of the Army Wilbur M. Brucker, onetime Republican governor of Michigan.

"Now they can't accuse me of not sending up smoke signals for each party," he chuckled, puffing away. "Donkey and elephant, both."

Eyes crinkled at the corners through long acquaintance with dirty weather and other perils on the Inland Seas, he stared out across the five miles of whitecapped water that formed the Straits between Lake Huron and Lake Michigan. With half a glance he could identify and state the destination of every stick afloat in the hustle of shipping bound around the tip of Michigan's mitten under the Bridge.

"There goes a limestone carrier from Calcite to Chicago," he told the School Reporter, pointing out each boat with his longstemmed Irish pipe. "Here comes a grain carrier fresh out of the Soo Canal from Fort

William or Port Arthur up on the Canadian shore of Lake Superior. She's bound down Lake Michigan for the flour mills of the Midwest with half a million bushels of wheat in her hold. It took thirty freight trains, each pulling a long string of cars, to deliver enough wheat to the docks to load that lake freighter down to her Plimsoll mark."

"Thirty freight *trains*," the School Reporter wrote, underlining the last word.

"Here comes another *long ship passing*," the Watchman said, underlining the last three words with his voice. "The bulk carrier *Edmund Fitzgerald*. She was launched slaunchwise in typical Great Lakes style in June, 1958, the dedication time of Mackinac Bridge, tumbling sideways into the Detroit River to become the new monarch of the Inland Seas. Son, you're looking at an eight-million-dollar giant, 729 feet and three inches long, longer than all but a count-on-your-fingers number of ocean-going liners. There'll never be a bigger boat on fresh water, because U.S. Army engineers have ruled that 730 feet is as long as any ship can be and still use the Soo Locks, the key link in the St. Lawrence Seaway."

In his excitement about the big freighters the Watchman let his pipe go out. "These long ships passing down below," he went on, "helped build the Bridge. They carried the ore down from the Marquette and Mesabi iron ranges of Lake Superior, 24 thousand tons of iron ore a trip, and they took it to the steel mills on the Lower Lakes where it was made into the girders and sections of Long Mack. I guess you might say Mackinac Bridge was Great Lakes born and bred!"

With his clay pipe whose bowl was ornamented by a tiny golden harp and green shamrock, the Watchman

pointed out other vessels in the endless flotillas that
passed though the Straits of Mackinac while cars from
every state in the union and province in Canada passed
high above the Crossroads of the Great Lakes.

"The big passenger boat is an excursion liner bringing up a convention crowd from Detroit to Mackinac
Island's Grand Hotel, biggest wooden building and
longest front porch in the world. That Coast Guard
vessel is the Great White Lady of the Upper Lakes, the
ice-breaker Mackinaw, and, like her sister ships up in
the Arctic and Antarctic, she can make a speed of four
knots through ice more than four feet thick, solid
winter *blue* ice, not spring punk. That other boat with
the big iron jaw plowing across the Straits from Mackinaw City to St. Ignace is quite an ice buster herself,
the railroad-car ferry Ste. Marie. The Mackinaw and
the Ste. Marie played an important part in building
Mackinac Bridge, too. They helped keep navigation
open in the spring so that long ships could start delivering their ore to the steel plants down at Gary, Indiana,
and Ambridge, Pennsylvania, where the steelwork was
fabricated by the American Bridge Division of the U. S.
Steel Corporation."

The School Reporter kept jotting down notes in a
shorthand all his own. His eyes were big with what
they saw far below on the broad waters. "They look
like toy boats in a bathtub from up here," he commented,
and then sucked in his breath as he spotted what appeared to be white gulls winging across the Straits.
"Look at those two sailboats!"

"The yawl with the all-aluminum hull and poles
shining in the sun is the 58-foot *Dyna* out of Green Bay,
Wisconsin," the Watchman said. "She kicked up a clean
pair of heels to all the racing yachts in both the Mack-

inacs the year the Long Crossing was completed, and then she celebrated the dedication year of the Bridge by turning the same trick again, making a clean sweep of the world's longest races over fresh-water, two years in a row, '57 and '58."

The School Repoter's pencil kept busy. "How far do they race?"

"From Port Huron to Mackinac Island it's a cruise of 250 miles, and the Chicago to Mackinac that's been held every year for more than half a century covers 333 miles. Some of those wealthy sportsmen are real sailors," the Watchman admitted. "They ship rough-and-tumble windjammer crews aboard the eighty or so racing hulls that take part in both Mackinacs each July."

"Is that other sailboat one of the Mackinac racers too?"

"No, son, that's the schooner *Heather* with Kreigh Collins at the helm and his four boys manning the sails. You can't tell from way up here, but he's got a build and beard just like one of the Vikings he draws in his comic strip every week — Kevin the Bold."

"Kevin the Bold?" The School Reporter acted as if he could not believe his ears. "Why, that's in the paper we take, and it's just about my favorite!"

"Last time I saw Kreigh, he told me that almost a hundred papers carry Kevin the Bold, the Detroit *News*, the Chicago *Tribune*, lots of them."

"And he draws it right aboard his boat?"

"Sure, he's got one part of the main cabin rigged out into a shipshape studio, with a drawing board and all kinds of tools of his trade that can be brought out for business or tucked away as neat as the compartment in a seachest. Kreigh's probably drawing an adventure of Kevin the Bold in his mind right now, and he'll sketch it out on drafting paper this evening and mail it to the syndicate at Cleveland from his next port of call on the Lakes."

Sighting of the *Heather* and mention of Kreigh Collins launched the Watchman into a talk about what he called the old and the new Northwest Passage. The Mackinac Bridge was the twentieth-century's Northwest Passage, so he said, but he told the story of the fabled Northwest Passage first.

Take the old Lake Captain's word for it, and Columbus was a Johnny-come-lately to the New World and the *Mayflower* brought the Pilgrim Fathers to Plymouth Rock several centuries behind the times. Ages before Queen Isabella pawned her jewels, the wild Irish, whose patron saint was St. Brendan the Sailor, set out from the Emerald Isle in their skin-boats called *curragh* and blazed a trail across the great whale path more than six hundred miles to Iceland. Greenland lay only one hundred and eighty miles beyond that, and from Greenland the bog-trotters could walk the rest of the way to the mainland of North America, but there is no record that they did.

The Norsemen took over where the Irish left off, and perhaps a captive Irish bride of Leif the Lucky gave Eric the Red the inheritance of flaming hair that sparked the advance of the Vikings across unexplored seas.

Watchman (lighting his pipe) : Picture one square sail, scudding an open boat across a wilderness of water with a bearded giant steering by sun and stars, while chickens squawked on deck and a seasick cow served as a foghorn. Salt spray froze on the spears and shields, and ice made the oars weigh a ton, but the Norsemen just raised their tankards and roared: "Skoal to the westward! Skoal!"

They chartered a course from Iceland to Greenland

to Newfoundland, to the shores of what they called Vinland. They thought it was an island, but, as the Watchman said, they were short on geography but long on the stuff it takes to map out a continent.

The Vikings went straight 'as an arrow into the heartland of America. They ventured across the Gulf of the St. Lawrence and sailed the mighty river past Quebec. When they came to a rapids, they portaged their goods around the rocks and angry water, built another ship, and sailed on.

Following this paddle-and-portage route and hoisting a patchwork sail, the Norsemen took the St. Lawrence Seaway to Minnesota. There they set up the traditional runic stone, marking the westernmost point of their expedition:

"We are eight Swedes and twenty-two Norwegians on an exploratory trip from Vinland through the West. We had camped by a lake with two skerries one day's journey north from this stone. We were away and fished one day. When we came back, we found ten of our men red with blood and dead. Ave Maria, save us from evil."

Watchman (soberly): A prayer for help, son, echoing down the ages to us.

Reporter (same tone): Yes, sir, but they blazed a trail for everybody to follow.

The descendants of the early comers, the Irish, the Norwegians, the Swedes, the Finns, eventually came to the lands and waters their forefathers had explored and, in the nineteenth century, they helped clear the forests of Michigan, Wisconsin, and Minnesota, they played their part in building the Soo Canal, they worked the iron and copper mines of the Lake Superior region.

The first Vikings navigated the St. Lawrence Seaway

five hundred years before Columbus began the trip that
sailed him into schoolbooks, and when the Pilgrims
landed at Plymouth they were welcomed by local Indians who wore jewelry and used fish hooks made from
copper mined by Algonquin mound builders out of
open pits located on Isle Royale and along the Keweenaw Peninsula.

In the early days of discovery, a fever shook the world
to find the mythical Northwest Passage. America was
regarded as hardly more than a stepping stone. All the
explorers had a mania to push on and get to the Orient.
Asia was supposed to be just over the next hill, around
the next bend in the stream.

A London merchant who prospered during the reign
of Queen Elizabeth the First expected to mail a letter
to China and have it arrive in three months by way of
America. Captain George Waymouth sailed the *Discovery* into Hudson Straits with members of his crew
dressed up to impress the Chinese. When Thomas
James set out from England to trace the fabulous passage
he was so sure of accomplishing his aim that he carried
a letter from Britain's king addressed to Japan's emperor.

The French hunted the Northwest Passage too, the
Black Robes or Jesuits leading the way, with the trap-
pers and traders close on their heels. They had the
homing instinct and went straight for the heartland
along the St. Lawrence. They had the five great un-
salted seas in their grasp and the Mississippi was their
good right arm long before any other nationality had
more than a beachhead on the North American continent.

Courage they had, and color. Jean Nicolet cruised
the Lakes through the Straits of Mackinac to Green Bay,
Wisconsin, where he stepped ashore in full regalia to
meet the potentates of Asia. His brilliant Oriental robe

of damask embroidered with birds and flowers impressed the Ottawas and Chippewas.

"This must be China," he declared, planting the French flag in the sand and firing off a brace of pistols to impress the breech-clouted natives. "Lead me to your Emperor."

Like a will-o'-the-Wisp, the legend of the Northwest Passage had beckoned and lured brave men to adventurous deeds, to the housing of a continent, to the building of the Soo Canal, to such an accomplishment as Mackinac Bridge.

"There never was any real Northwest Passage to the Orient," the Watchman told the School Reporter. "The only place it existed was in men's minds, and hearts, but that's the important place; that's where the *Long Crossing* always begins. This country would still be a howling wilderness if men hadn't followed their dreams. There's one thing that every voyageur of yesterday shared with every builder of this bridge of today; they all had faith in finding what they wanted around the next bend in the stream!"

New Northwest Passage, the Reporter wrote in his notepad, and then stared at the highway that Mackinac Bridge lifted across the Straits, above the long ships passing now and the phantom sails of long ago.

Four

Newsboy at Brooklyn Bridge

Where has the young buck gone?
See where the far star gleams?
There is the glow of his campfire;
Watch him, so brave with dreams!
                    Adventures of Captain McCargo

WITH HIS MIND still on the voyageurs and chevaliers who
dared pathless forests and uncharted waters to search out
the old Northwest Passage, the Watchman on Mackinac
Bridge scratched a kitchen match on the seat of his pants
to light his pipe and said between slow puffs:

"The French of the North have never been great
fighters nor great hunters, in the terms of Anglo-Saxon
frontiersmen, but they have laughed in farther places."

Somehow the words drew a picture for the School
Reporter, a picture of a burly French Canadian, red-
sashed and eagle-feathered, toting a canoe around a
remote portage and laughing at a stretch of rapids running wild as white-maned horses down a green-sloped
hill. "Laughed in farther places," he repeated. "It
almost tells a whole story."

The Watchman nodded. "Stewart Edward White
said that, and he knew this North Country like a book.
Fact, he wrote books about it, *The Riverman*, *The
Blazed Trail*, some of the best. But I think he would
agree with me that the farthest travelers can belong to
any nationality and that the farthest travels aren't made

by canoe or by bearclaw snowshoe but by dreams. There's no place a dream can't go, son, and nothing a dreamer can't do. The Soo Canal was built by dreams and so was this bridge. A couple of boys, a hundred years apart in time, dreamed of growing up and building great public works, and their dreams came true, only fifty miles apart in geography, at the two historic crossings on the Upper Great Lakes."

"The Straits of Mackinac and the St. Mary's River between the American and the Canadian Soo," the School Reporter volunteered in the quick and cheerful voice of one who has learned his lesson by heart.

"Talk about seven league boots or magic carpets," the old Lake Captain went on, "they have to play second fiddle to dreams. If a boy knows how to dream, and is willing to work to make his dream come true, he's got Aladdin's Lamp at his elbow and he can say *Open, Sesame* to any door that's shut against him."

With the School Reporter hanging on every word, the Watchman on Mackinac Bridge told about the two boys who had dreamed the world's greatest canal and the world's greatest suspension span into engineering realities. They were not much alike, these youngsters. The one became a large, two-fisted, self-made man with very little formal education. His canal gangs affectionately called him "Young Mister Big." The other, undernourished in youth, subscribed to all the muscle-building exercises on the market but never reached any great size. Forced to rely on brains rather than brawn, he earned four college diplomas and, by the time he began work on the Long Crossing, there were twenty honorary degrees behind his name.

Reporter (admiringly) : Boy, he must have been a real egghead!

Watchman (chuckling: Yup, I guess you could call

David B. Steinman, LL.D., L.H.D., Litt.D., D.Eng.,
Sc.D., D.C.E., Ph.D., F.R.S.A., etc., an egghead of the
first water!

From reading the book *Young Mister Big* in the
school library, the Reporter already knew the story of
Charles T. Harvey, the twenty-three year old traveling
salesman for the Fairbanks Scales Company of St. Johns-
bury, Vermont, whose employers had sent him to the
North Country for a rest-cure and who had taken a two-
year "vacation" promoting and building the backwoods
canal that turned out to be busier and more important
than the Panama and the Suez canals put together.

Watchman: Never had a lick of college training,
never built so much as a wooden sidewalk or a white
picket fence in his life before, but he had a knack of
getting things done because he could live up to the brag
of a real Mackinac man.

> *Got a fist like a hammer,*
> *Got a foot like a feather,*
> *Got a heart like an Indian drum!*

It was a curious tie between Charles T. Harvey and
David B. Steinman that the future canal builder had
started his career at the age of twelve by attempting a
backyard bridge in his Connecticut hometown. As
he described the project to a grownup:

"It's a bridge across the brook, sir. I had to pick a
kind of narrow place, and it won't be able to hold up
a regular wagon or team of horses or anything like
that, but it's going to be a real bridge. I mean, it will
hold me up, and a dog, and — you know." His voice
rose with excitement. "I ran errands down at the saw-
mill and got them to pay me in laths. The framework
for the bridge is made out of laths. It's a brand-new

construction idea that nobody ever thought of before. I figured it out myself."

Most grownups smiled tolerantly at young Harvey's enthusiasm and all of his playmates made fun of his big ideas, teasing him to go swimming or fishing with them instead of wasting his time on a "toy" bridge, but there was an oldtime expert in the neighborhood who came to inspect the structure. When it bore up under a wheelbarrow loaded with stones, he raised his plug hat in a cheer.

"Never budged," Mr. Nichols chortled. "Couldn't have done a better job myself." His gnarled fingers reached out to give Charles Harvey a grave handshake. "You've got dreams in your eyes, son. Most boys get those dreams shaken loose by the time they grow up. Only a few men are able to make their boyhood dreams come true. I'm betting you've got what it takes. There's room out West in the Great Lakes country for more railroads and such than a monkey could shake a stick at in a month of Sundays. Tell you what, son. First big construction job you get, send for yours truly, L.L. Nichols of the old Erie Canal, and I'll come out of retirement quicker than scat!"

"Thank you, Sir." The boy pumped the veteran engineer's right hand solemnly. "I will send for you, Mr. Nichols, because I'll need a good right-hand man, especially on my first big job!"

The dream came true, and Young Mister Big lived up to his word by sending for Mr. Nichols to help him dig a canal and install ship locks around the roaring Falls of St. Mary's where the floodwaters of Lake Superior spilled down a rocky channel to prevent boat passage between the greatest of all lakes and her strapping big sisters below.

At the age of twelve, Charles T. Harvey had made

up his mind about his entire future. He intended to become a famous construction engineer. His name will forever be associated with the hardworking Cinderella of the world's major canals instead of with a bridge, but on his way to and from the mighty ditch at Sault Ste. Marie a hundred years ago, he may have paced the deck of his steamboat and day-dreamed of bridging the water barrier between Michigan's two peninsulas.

However, the boy destined to make giant steps across the place where Lake Huron and Lake Michigan tipped their hats to each other was born in the city of great bridges, New York. In 1887, the very year of his birth, the Grand Hotel on Mackinac Island was dedicated, and in his speech at the formal ceremonies Commodore Vanderbilt said:

"What this area now needs is a bridge across the Straits."

Tiny David B. Steinman had been spanked into the world under the very shadows of the story-book bridge that leaped across the bustling East River between Manhattan Island and Brooklyn. The son of immigrant parents who had crossed the ocean from the Old Country to seek out the promise upheld to all comers by the Statue of Liberty in New York Harbor, his childhood was spent under the influence of the inspiring bridge completed four years before his birth.

Davey Steinman grew from infancy to boyhood under the spell of Brooklyn Bridge. The lights on the bridge at night were the stars under which he slept in his cradle. His dreams were haunted by the clock-round traffic noises on the bridge, from the clomp and creak of market wagons at sunrise to the click and whisk of fashionable buggies returning from theater suppers at midnight. The shadows of the bridge fell across the floor he crept and played on. When he learned to walk,

his first uncertain steps were taken toward the bridge.
When his older sister taught him to spell out words,
the primer and beginner's arithmetic book that they
used was the sign at the bridge:

TOLLS

1 Cent For Pedestrians, $.05 For Cows,
10 - 30c For Horse-Drawn Vehicles

An all-seeing Providence linked the boy's life to the
bridge, a Providence that would lead to his own name
being engraved on a bronze tablet there, in memory of
his converting its two-lane, horse-and-buggy traffic to
modern, six-lane passenger car traffic. An all-seeing
Providence was reaching out, even in his earliest childhood, to link the bridge that inspired his boyhood dream
to the bridge that would represent the crowning accomplishment of his manhood.

In Michigan, in the decade of Davey Steinman's birth
and the building of the bridge that electrified the world,
a newspaper editorial in the Grand Traverse *Herald,* a
hundred miles below the Straits of Mackinac, talked
about the possibility of building a bridge over the
Crossroads of the Great Lakes. Later a local merchant
decorated his newspaper advertisements with an artist's
woodcut of the Brooklyn Bridge, under the caption:
"A Glimpse of the Future." Below the woodcut in
the ad was inscribed: "Proposed Bridge Across the
Straits of Mackinac."

The merchant in Michigan had vision that saw into
the next century, and the boy on Manhattan Island in
New York had a dream. The Steinmans were a poor
family, barely able to make ends meet. The biggest
thing about little Davey was his eyes, forever asking
questions of the world. When he was only three years

old, the youngest of seven children, he showed talent
in numbers, figuring out that he and his brothers and
sisters were alternately boy and girl spaced three years
apart, and that their ages therefore made a perfect
arithmetical progression: 3, 6, 9, 12, 15, 18, 21.

Although the experiments of a boy named Tom Edison at Port Huron, Michigan, had resulted in bringing
electric light bulbs to Manhattan, the childhood of
David Steinman had no acquaintance with such luxury.
The family had one kerosene lamp for three rooms,
later replaced by a single gas light. They had to go to
bed at eight, to save money on gas. This early retiring
habit remained with the boy through later years. Even
in his college days, he would fall asleep, reading a book,
at eight o'clock.

Davey learned the alphabet earlier than most youngsters, spelling out the words on the Brooklyn Bridge sign
until he knew them by heart. While walking alone,
he taught himself to read street signs and the lettering
on shop windows. Very soon he escaped from the drab
poverty of his daily surroundings into the romantic
world of books. He skipped over the top of the long
words, figuring out what they meant by the familiar
words he recognized, and by the age of five he had read
most of Jules Verne, Alexandre Dumas, and Victor Hugo,
with quite a bit of Mark Twain and Henty. In short
order he went on into Scott, Thackeray, and Dickens.

However, it was in the world of numbers that Davey
really shined. As soon as he had been taught to count
up to ten, he took off under his own power and worked
out for himself the elementary arithmetic steps: addition,
subtraction, multiplication, long division.

When he was five years old, his older sister took Davey
on a visit to her school to show him off to her teachers
and to the principal. He could rattle off the powers

of two — 2, 4, 8, 16, 32 — up to a million. They tested
him with such problems as 17 times 19, or 27 x 43, all
in mental arithmetic.

Reporter (whistling in amazement): Boy, he must
have been a whiz! I couldn't even begin to do those
problems in my head!

Watchman (beaming in sympathy) : In your head?
Son, I'd be lucky to figure out the right answers with
five sharp pencils and a whole scratch pad!

As a reward for answering the difficult problems, a
teacher gave Davey and his sister a ten-cent box that
held three charlotte russe. There was no ice-box at home
but the weather was cold, so they kept the treat on the
fire escape, taking only a nibble each day in order to
prolong the pleasure. Stretched out this way the treasured dessert lasted nearly three weeks.

Watchman: Dr. Steinman told me about it himself
one time when he was up here checking on Long Mack.
He said he could still remember how that charlotte
russe tasted.

Reporter (his own mouth watering) : Ummmm.

At the age of seven, Davey Steinman had to go out
on the street and bring in his share of money to keep
the family alive. He and an older brother became newsboys. Each day they trudged down to Newspaper
Square, located at the entrance to Brooklyn Bridge.
Here they invested their pennies in papers, which cost
two for a cent at the printing plants and could be sold
to the public at the regular rate of one cent apiece.
Doubling their money in this way, the boys made as
much as fifty cents an afternoon to take home.

Standing on the corner, selling his papers, David B.
Steinman, seven years old, stared up at Brooklyn Bridge.
To him it was something more than concrete and metal,
it was a thing alive. He saw the steel members of the

suspension span flexing their mighty muscles as they
upheld the great loads of stone and cable, the beams
and girders, stretching, twisting, bending, the wires hum-
ming songs of defiance against the wind.

The boy with the slight build and the big eyes had
been feeling something grow in his heart day after day
while he stood near the entrance to the bridge, and he
wanted to confide his secret to someone. All of a sudden
one afternoon, amid the rumbling of bridge traffic, foggy
up-river whistles, and shrill cries of "Paper, mister?" he
pointed to the great structure overhead and told the
other newsboys:

"Someday I'm going to build bridges like that!"

They laughed at him, and when he stuck to his guns
and defended his dream, they gave him a nickname.
They called him "Crazy Kid."

Five

Walt Whitman and the Brooklyn Bridge

Bite off more than you can chew — and chew it.
Lay out more than you can do — and do it.
Hitch your wagon to a star,
Hold your seat — and there you are.
U. S. Naval Institute

As THE WATCHMAN on Mackinac Bridge told the School Reporter about the early life of David B. Steinman, he brought up the name of Old Cap Sparhawk, the legendary Great Lakes character whose paddlewheel steamboat the *Prairie Dew* had been of service in building the Soo Canal by hauling immigrant workers up from Chicago or Buffalo to the diggings bossed by Young Mister Big. When the peppery old gent in the stovepipe hat and the Prince Albert coat hit port, he always took a string of admiring youngsters in tow and he had a favorite speech he never failed to make to them once the rock candy that bulged his pockets made the rounds:

"Boys, did you ever think that this world, with all its wealth and woe, with all its mines and mountains, oceans, seas and rivers, with all its shipping, its steamboats, railroads, and magnetic telegraphs, with all its millions of men and all the science and progress of the ages, will soon be given over to boys of the present age, boys like you? Believe it, lads, and look abroad upon your inheritance, and get ready to enter upon your possession. The presidents, kings, governors, statesmen,

philosophers, ministers, teachers, engineers, men of the future, they're all boys now, remember!"

Whether or not Davey Steinman ever heard of Old Cap Sparhawk, the rambunctious sidekick of young Captain Mc-Cargo, the words of the *Prairie Dew's* skipper sounded in his heart. He might be the smallest boy on the block today, but he intended to grow up into the biggest bridgebuilder in the world tomorrow!

Times when he was free from school and not selling papers, he liked to walk down to the toe of Manhattan Island where California and transatlantic clippers lay at the docks. Sailing ships still outnumbered steamboats in those days, and his young eyes thrilled to the now-vanished glory of proud masts and clouds of canvas blown in from the seven seas.

All poets are boys at heart and Walt Whitman, the giant among American poets, had watched the identical scene day after day, and then written about it in his poem called "Crossing Brooklyn Ferry." Davey Steinman could look out across the forest of shipping and echo one of the poet's lines: "Ah, what can ever be more stately and more admirable to me than mast-hemmed Manhattan!"

There were stirrings of poetry in the boy, too, and

perhaps a measure of calculation in the sharp eyes that watched the ferries pull out across New York harbor for Hoboken or Staten Island. The suspension bridge that had put a birthmark on his inner nature had made the Brooklyn ferry service obsolete. He stared out across the water and thought to himself:

"I'm going to be a bridgebuilder. It's going to be my business to put ferry boats out of business, all over the world."

Every chance that offered, he took a walk across the Brooklyn Bridge, memorizing each detail of its construction by heart, from the anchored pylons to the soaring cables. Standing on the promenade high above the East River, he could see the harbor, the shipping, the Statue of Liberty, the sky scrapers of that era, all the sights Walt Whitman had glimpsed from the Brooklyn Ferry. The old grey poet might well have had a young disciple like Davey Steinman in mind when he wrote:

> Just as you look on the numberless masts of ships and the
> thick-stemmed pipes of steamboats, I looked.
> I too many and many a time crossed the river of old,
> Saw the white sails of schooners and sloops, saw the ships
> at anchor,
> The sailors at work in the rigging or out astride the spars,
> The flags of all nations, the falling of them at sunset,
> These and all else were to me the same as they are to you. . . .
> What is it then between us?
> I too lived, Brooklyn of ample hills was mine,
> I too walked the streets of Manhattan island, and bathed in
> the waters around it,
> I too felt the curious abrupt questionings stir within me.

There is no doubt that little Davey Steinman felt "curious abrupt questionings" stir within himself on Brooklyn Bridge. In his eyes the bridge was a poem, as fine as anything Walt Whitman ever had written.

He intended to write poems of the same kind, poems written in stone and in steel across broad waters.

One afternoon he came home late because he had not only walked across, and studied, the Brooklyn Bridge over the East River but also High Bridge and Washington Bridge over the Harlem River. He was tired and hungry, his shoes were scuffed from scrambling down embankments and trying to get toeholds on bridge girders. His father, heavy factory-calloused hands clenched in anger, glared at him.

"What you done? Where you been?"

"Nothing wrong, father. Just walking around town."

"Scallywagging over bridges again, huh?" Whack! "Wasting time and wearing out shoe leather." Whack! "Maybe this'll learn you." Whack!

Whipped and sent to bed without his supper, Davey Steinman never nursed any grudge against his stern, hard-working father. The next time he walked across Brooklyn Bridge, he still had his heart in his eyes, but he carried his precious shoes very carefully in his hands.

And the Bridge felt more wonderful than ever, under his bare feet.

Six

Steve Brodie and Horatio Alger

He either fears his fate too much,
Or his deserts are small,
Who dares not put it to the touch
To win or lose it all.

"LET'S WET OUR WHISTLES," said the Watchman on Mackinac Bridge, hauling two bottles of red pop out of a thermos pail and handing one to the school reporter. "It's raspberry shrub, fruit juice and sweetened water, the strongest drink Charles Harvey ever allowed himself and his canal gangs. I offered a bottle to Dr. Steinman once when the Long Crossing was under construction."

School Reporter (between long swallows): Did he like it?

Watchman (chuckling): Gulped it down almost as fast as you. Said if raspberry shrub helped build the Soo Canal, it ought to give a lift to anybody building the Mackinac Bridge!

Then the Watchman told the story of the Bowery character who leaped himself into a legend and became part of American folklore by jumping off the Brooklyn Bridge. Once a bootblack at a cheap hotel where the bridge entrance had been built, Steve Brodie added a new phrase to the English language with his daring stunt. Anyone taking a long chance was described as "doing a Brodie."

However, there were a few Doubting Thomases who

maintained that Steve Brodie and his friends, in common
with most Irishmen, never let the truth spoil a good
story.   They said, in fact, that nothing but a clothes-
store dummy had made the leap from the bridge and
that Brodie, lurking at an East River dock, had swum
underwater to the spot of the dummy's splash where he
was fished out by the crew of a passing barge.

But the doubters were squelched.   Brodie's stunt
caught the public imagination, and the story grew in
magic telling across the impressionable years of Davey
Steinman's childhood.   He heard the legend, over and
over again, and every time it drew his attention closer
to the bridge.

His leap for life made Brodie so popular that a bever-
age company sponsored him in a refreshment parlor on
the Bowery, and the place soon became very popular.
The main attraction was an enormous East River landscape done in oils.   This loud-colored monstrosity
showed Brodie halfway in the air between the bridge
and the water.   The picture was pointed out by Steve's
friends as proof positive of his feat, and they backed it
up with a framed affidavit from the barge captain who
claimed to have pulled Brodie from the tide.

A few years later the legend proved of such mass
appeal that the stage play, "On the Bowery," starring
Steve Brodie himself, opened in Philadelphia and then
came across the Brooklyn Bridge to the People's Theater
on Manhattan Island where it brought down the house
with applause.   The thrilling climax, for which the
crowds waited in breathless suspense, came in two scenes
of Act III.   The first of these scenes showed the villain
Thurlow Bleeckman hurl the heroine Blanche from
the walkway of the bridge into the river far below, while
Steve and other horrified witnesses looked on, aghast.

"There's one chance in a thousand that you can save her," cried a spectator, not anxious to leave the security of the bridge walkway himself. "Will you take that chance, Brodie?"

"You bet your life I will!" replied the brave fellow. And over he went.

The following scene showed a quick change to the river level with Steve plunging down through a trap door onto a darkened and dry-as-dust stage while hands tossed buckets of rock salt to fake the appearance of spray thrown up by his leap.

The curtain always went down on pandemonium. Bouquets were thrown on the stage. Steve Brodie ruled as the hero of the hour. The title of the play became the hit of the nation:

> The Bow'ry, the Bow'ry!
> They say such things
> And they do strange things
> On the Bow'ry! The Bow'ry!
> I'll never go there any more!

In the same year that saw rave notices of Steve Brodie's stage play appear in the New York papers, David B. Steinman was a seven-year-old newsboy selling those same papers at Brooklyn Bridge and voicing his own proud dream between shouts of "Paper, mister?" No amount of ridicule could stop him from saying:

"Some day I'm going to build bridges like that!"

The other boys who laughed at him as he gazed up at the massive beams of Brooklyn Bridge could not be blamed for failing to see that the dreams in Davey Steinman's eyes would turn into the solid reality of more than four hundred bridges on five continents, the only exception being Africa. There was no prophet handy to tell his jeering companions that this newsboy, clutching pennies in his fist, would one day hold a check for a hundred million dollars, more money than had ever been paid for any bridge in history, the price of the Long Crossing, Mackinac Bridge.

Even as a boy of seven, Davey Steinman had definite ideas of how to get ahead in the world, and these ideas did not include show-off stunts of the Steve Brodie kind. Nor, unlike his fellow newsboys, did he pay any attention to the sure-fire success stories in the Horatio Alger books that were so popular at the time. The 135 titles in the Horatio Alger list sold a total of 200 million copies, but Davey Steinman never boosted the sales because he had no confidence in their quick rags-to-riches formula. He relied on a slower and harder plan.

Horatio Alger had first-hand acquaintance with the kind of boys who sold newspapers alongside Davey Steinman at Brooklyn Bridge. In fact, after the publication of *Ragged Dick, or, Street Life in New York,* an all-time best-seller ranking with *Uncle Tom's Cabin* and *Gone With the Wind,* Alger was invited by the superintendent of the Newsboys' Lodging House on Manhattan to make his home there, and he moved into that charitable institution for many years, living there during the period when Davey Steinman sold newspapers, and encouraging his young companions at the Home by writing books that told them to *Work and Win,* to *Plan and Prosper,* to *Do and Dare,* to *Wait and Hope,* to *Strive and Succeed,* to be *Brave and Bold,* to be *Strong and Steady,* to be *Slow and Sure,* to be *Frank and Fearless,* in which case they were *Bound to Rise,* guaranteed of *Forging Ahead,* and sure of *Falling in with Fortune.*

No doubt the Horatio Alger book titles inspired a certain number of boys. A successful business man might trace his rise back to the boyhood day when he dipped into the pages of some such volumes as *Mark Ma-*

*son's Victory, or, The Trials and Triumphs of a Tele-
graph Boy; Sam's Chance, and How He Improved It; The
Errand Boy, or, How Phil Brent Won Success; Struggling
Upward, or, Luke Larkin's Luck,* and so forth.   This
type of reading fare was fine for boys who aimed at
the commonplace ambition of becoming rich men, but
it had no appeal for boys with the creative spark whose
ultimate goal was enriching mankind.

Horatio Alger's heroes were all nice, bright, depend-
able young men with a complete set of virtues, and yet
they were seldom gifted with any talent, and no Alger
hero was recorded as *Making His Mark* in the world
by developing his talents through years of study and hard
practical experience.   To attract the average reader and
sell millions of copies, a much easier way to fame and
fortune had to be shown, a way that any plucky, well-
scrubbed young nomad of the streets might stumble upon at any moment.

Was it Nelson the Newsboy who won a place in Wall
Street by rescuing the pretty daughter of a banker as
she was being hurtled to an untimely death by the foaming steeds of her runaway carriage in Central Park?
As for Phil the Fiddler, he never showed much improvement as a musician, but toward the end of the novel he
conveniently dropped from exhaustion in a snowbank
where he was found, thawed out, and adopted by a
wealthy physician whose son of about the same age had
just died.

But the classic case, the perfect model of all Horatio
Alger heroes, was Ragged Dick.   He wandered through
most of his novel, right up to the next-to-last chapter,
without accomplishing much of anything except for
taking the reader on a tour of little old New York.   Like
Steve Brodie, Ragged Dick was a bootblack and he also

took his own leap to fame and fortune in the neighborhood of Brooklyn Bridge.

Running an errand to Brooklyn, he boarded the ferry
and stood at the rail in the stern of the boat as it pulled
out across the river. Beside him was a gentleman with
a little girl of eight and a boy of six. The boy crept
beneath the protective chain and fell over the stern of
the ferry into the foaming wake. As Horatio Alger
described the scene:

> At the child's scream, the father looked up, and, with a
> cry of horror, sprang to the edge of the boat. He would
> have plunged in, but, being unable to swim, would only
> have endangered his own life, without being able to save
> his child.
> "My child!" he exclaimed in anguish — "Who will save
> my child? A thousand — ten thousand dollars to any one
> who will save him!"

Among the few who saw the child fall was our hero,
an expert swimmer, a fact kept a secret from the reader
until this timely moment. The author also hastened to
tell his readers that Ragged Dick was not influenced by
the father's offer of a liberal reward. He would have
plunged to the rescue anyway. Over he went.

> Little Johnny had already risen once, and gone under
> for the second time, when our hero plunged in. He reached
> him none too soon. Just as he was sinking for the third and
> last time, he caught him by the jacket.
> "Put your arms round my neck," said Dick.

Ragged Dick had quite a struggle keeping the child
afloat but, as in the case of Steve Brodie, a small boat
happened along and the crew lifted him and his burden
from the water. They were brought to the ferry dock
on the Brooklyn side where the child's father clasped
Dick's hand and said with emotion:

"My brave boy, I owe you a debt I can never repay. But for your timely service I should now be plunged into an anguish which I cannot think of without a shudder."

Our hero was ready enough to speak on most occasions, but always felt awkward when he was praised.

"It wasn't any trouble," he said modestly. "I can swim like a top."

As a reward for being on the spot to rescue Johnny, Ragged Dick became Richard Hunter, Esq., overnight. The grateful father made him a clerk in his banking house, and any reader of Horatio Alger novels could read between the lines that the hero in due time would marry the banker's daughter.

This lucky road to success suited the wishful thinking and day-dreaming of the average newsboy, but it was far from enough to suit a Davey Steinman. He knew he had talents, and he made up his mind to improve them by the best education possible, and by directed effort instead of trusting in lucky breaks. He was a dreamer, but his dreams were based on the solid inspirational reality of the Brooklyn Bridge and not on the glib promises in dime novels.

As a sign that a boy's thinking may be better than a grownup's way of life, two tragic events happened while Davey was still in his early years. Steve Brodie died a young man, victim of the beverages in his own refreshment parlor. And Horatio Alger, the man who had written the American success story over and over again, died a heartbroken failure. All his life he had dreamed of writing the great American novel. He never got much further than the title page, which someone saw on the desk in the room where he died. It was full of erasure marks and scratched-out words and half-finished sentences.

Watchman (pausing his story-telling to knock out his

pipe on Mackinac Bridge) : The book that Horatio Alger
spent so much wishful-thinking about but never got
around to writing, can you make a guess what it was
to be called?

Reporter (shaking his head): No, sir. What?

Watchman: Its title was *Tomorrow,* and I guess that
points up the moral to the whole story, without me adding another word. Tell me something. If you were
choosing up sides between Steve Brodie and Horatio
Alger or Charles T. Harvey and David B. Steinman,
which would you take?

Reporter (smiling out loud) : I'd take another bottle
of raspberry shrub.

Watchman (diving into the thermos pail) : Son, you
just said a mouthful!

Seven

The Steam Engine's Left-Handed Monkey Wrench

Where does the young buck ride,
Swift as the lost wind blows?
Where are the tracks of his pony?
Only the skyline knows.

Capt. McCargo

LOLLING BACK IN his captain's chair on the approach to the Long Crossing, the Watchman on the Bridge pointed out a parking area below in Machinaw City. "See that old-fashioned touring car down there, son, the one with the green body and the brass radiator and the shamrocks painted on the doors?"

The School Reporter stared at the quaint sight below. "You mean the funny-looking automobile with no top, the one that's got wooden spoked wheels and tires not much bigger than the ones on my kid sister's bike?"

"Son," replied the old Lake captain in a voice full of dignity and wounded pride, "you're talking about my own private limousine. That's a historic vehicle, and it's got a special license to say so. The State of Michigan sort of pensions any car that gets to be more than twenty-five years old, and they rate special privileges. My Model-T, otherwise known as the Flivver or Tin Lizzie, has earned honorary retirement, like a man who's served his company or country well, and is entitled to be turned out to pasture with full support, but the old girl still

51

rides me around. She doesn't have to, she just does it for fun."

It amused the School Reporter to hear the grizzled Watchman talk about his old car as if it were a thing alive, and it impressed him too. "I'm sorry, sir," he apologized. "I didn't mean to make fun of your automoble. What's that shiny brass thing with the handle sticking up outside the driver's seat?"

"That's a hand-pump, old-time schooner whistle."

"A schooner whistle on an automobile?"

"Why not? It's going to take you and me across the Straits of Mackinac in a little while, and we'll whistle for passage as we sail over five miles of water while the long ships toot at us from below."

Reporter (thrilled and very careful how he speaks of the car): Will you really take me across in your historic vehicle?

Watchman: Yup, and before you finish taking all the notes on your Mackinac Bridge story for the school paper, you'll realize that the Model-T car made by Henry Ford was one of the most important builders of the Bridge. But right now I want to tell you about the Steam Engine and the left-handed monkey wrench.

Young David Steinman took to school the way a duck takes to water, and he skipped grades as if he were playing leapfrog. He always stood at the top of his class (in everything except height) and even in Sunday School he was such a star pupil that the minister had a favorite joking way of saying hello to him. He always smiled and said:

"Little David, play on your harp!"

Like any normal boy the future bridgebuilder enjoyed the adventures of Captain Nemo, Jean Valjean, Robinson Crusoe, the Count of Monte Cristo, Buffalo Bill, and Tom Sawyer, but he had special gifts and he could read his older brother's geometry textbook with as much pleasure as he read *Treasure Island*. At the age of ten he was entertaining and mystifying the other boys on his block with problems in algebra.

Each afternoon he finished his schoolwork in a few minutes, and then his classmates would come to his home for help. Sometimes they could hardly understand him, he spoke so fast. His mind worked so rapidly that his words, trying to keep pace, tumbled over themselves coming out of his mouth. As a result he lost his newsboy nickname of "Crazy Kid" and became known as "Steam Engine."

His ability and willingness to help other youngsters with their homework made David Steinman popular in school, but in the early grades he never achieved his one ambition. He yearned to be appointed a monitor, for washing slateboards and other classroom chores, but the teachers always passed over the boy in the hand-me-down clothes and the family-scissors haircut for the neater, better-dressed students. He day-dreamed of becoming a monitor, but, unlike his bridge-building dream, it never came true.

David's talent in mathematics was so high that sometimes even his teachers failed to appreciate it. A born mathematician, he carried the knowledge into his daily life. The Steinman house number was 625, and so he told his schoolmates:

"Our family lives on Fifth Street, at five to the fourth power."

One day he astonished his teacher by rattling off the fact that "the horizon is merely the line of tangency circumscribing that which is immediately visible." Horizons, he tried to explain to the class, were not boundaries; there was always more beyond. To a boy standing on the seashore, the horizon was a circle of

three-mile radius, but to a boy on a hill or a high building the horizon expanded.

Watchman: See what he was driving at, son? Take
a boy of today in New York, standing at the top of the
Empire State Building, and his horizon is enlarged to
a radius of forty-one miles. That's the mathematical
side of the idea, but you can figure out another side too,
and I think David Steinman was trying to point out to
his teacher and his classmates that if a boy has imagination there are no limits to the field of view. The horizon just keeps opening up.

Reporter (making a note): I see. It all depends on
how tall he dreams!

Some of David Steinman's ideas not only went over
the heads of his fellow students, but they were beyond
the scope of his grammar school teachers. One day the
class was given a problem which David answered cor-
rectly. The others copied from an answer book that
happened to have a misprint. Following the printed
answer book the teacher marked David wrong and the
rest of the class right.

"But, sir, there's a mistake in the answer book. I
can prove it!"

"So now you know more than the books?" the teacher
retorted with heavy sarcasm. "That'll be about enough
out of you, Steinman! Next thing we know you'll be
wanting to *write* the books, hmmmm?"

The class laughed, of course. All classes know by
instinct to laugh at all teachers' jokes, funny or not.
The boy did grow up to write books of many kinds,
including textbooks, biographies, and even a volume of
poems; and the recognition he never received in his own
grammar school days came to him later from grammar
school classes and teachers in many parts of the world.
More than all his honors, ranging from the Gold Medal

of the Americas to the scarlet riband of the French
Legion of Honor, the boy of yesterday treasured such
"awards of merit" as the following:

Dear Dr. Steinman:
   This is a letter from class 5-2 of P. S. 222, Brooklyn.
Our teacher is Miss Morgan.   Our class is working on a
bridge project.   We write stories and give reports on
bridges; some children in the class gave reports about you.
At home we build miniature bridges from wood and erector sets and bring them to school.   We have been working
on the bridge project for over a month and have eleven
bridges in the classroom.   After studying bridges everyone
of us thinks that you are probably one of the greatest
men in the world.   We are bringing the bridges to a teachers' meeting in the school, along with reports and displays;
also a report about you and the Mackinac Bridge.   The
whole class would be very pleased if we had your autograph to go with the other displays.   We would put it on
the very top of the pile.
   Some of us wish to be engineers when we grow up.   We
would be proud of ourselves if we could even do half of
your great accomplishments.   So if you will send your autograph to us we will be very grateful.   We know only a few
of the many bridges you have helped to build, but we are
learning more about you.   We have also written short
poems about bridges that we think sound very nice.
   We have read the articles about you in *The New York
Times* and try to be like you.
                              YOUR 32 ADMIRERS,
                              CLASS 5-2

Busy with the details of building a bridge for the
Iraqi Government over the Tigris River at romantic
Baghdad, busy building the first intercontinental bridge
in history — between Asia and Europe — across the
Bosporus from Istanbul, the onetime grammar school
boy who had never been considered quite good enough
to be chosen monitor of his class but had gone on in
grownup life to design and supervise construction
of the greatest engineering marvels since the Pyramids,

pushed all his work aside, not merely to send the requested autograph to Class 5-2 of Brooklyn, P. S. 222, but to carry on a long correspondence with the boys and girls about the beauty and joy in a good bridge.

In David Steinman's own grammar school days there were no such things as erector sets or do-it-yourself kits. An older friend introduced him to the wonders of chemistry when he was twelve. He had to build his own laboratory equipment — test-tube rack, retort stand, bunsen burner — and he saved his pennies to buy test tubes, glass tubing, and small supplies of chemicals. Then he gave demonstration lectures to the boys in the neighborhood, showing them how to make oxygen, hydrogen, ammonia, and sulphuric acid. With dilute sulphuric acid he had an invisible ink that he used for secret messages, in place of the average' youngster's onion or lemon juice formula.

He soon learned about electricity, too, and after more pinching of pennies, David managed to buy two dry batteries and some copper wire. This enabled him to perform experiments in electro-magnetism, and he built his own telegraph, galvanometer, electroscope, and so forth. When he had scrimped and saved enough money together from the bare-survival allowance he was given, going without lunches for weeks, he bought a small electric motor and proceeded to build a miniature auto-truck. Finding that the two dry batteries made the truck too heavy to run with a small motor, he substituted an overhead trolley wire to carry the current. Relieved of the weight of the dry batteries, the truck went automobubbling along, much to the delight of the youthful audience present on this historic occasion.

There were no model railroad trains or similar articles on the market at the time, and David Steinman's auto-truck created a sensation in the neighborhood.

However, the real automobiles that made rare appearances on city streets were met with hooted ridicule, and a certain young scientist was not above joining the rest of the crowd as they shouted out the classic taunt:

"Get a horse!"

Before David Steinman reached teen-age, several of his classroom works were selected by the New York Board of Education for permanent exhibit. One was a Dutch windmill electric fan and another was a combination rocking chair and cradle to make life easier for tired mothers.

Word about this got around. A newspaperman visited the school and interviewed the young inventor.

"I can't take full credit," David said, not with any false modesty but with a scientist's desire to reveal the exact truth. "I got the idea for the combination rocking chair and cradle from the notes on new patents in the *Scientific American*."

The newspaperman stared down at the slight figure with the big eyes and shook his head unbelievingly. "Don't tell me a kid like you can read that kind of stuff with the jawbreaker words?" Assured that the boy was a regular reader of the periodical, he went away, muttering to himself, and wrote a column on the editorial page of his paper about the youngster who read the *Scientific American* as if it were *Huckleberry Finn*.

When David Steinman started taking extra courses at night school, at the age of twelve, he took a class in applied mechanics and learned his first lessons in engineering. While the youngest boy in school watched with his big eyes getting even bigger, the instructor showed the class how a sheet of writing paper, curved into a cylinder, could support the weight of several books on top of the column, but the same sheet, folded flat to form a thin column, would buckle under the weight of a single book.

In another demonstration that the future builder of suspension bridges never forgot, the instructor showed how a strip of paper, one inch wide, could carry the weight of several pounds if they were hung from the bottom of it, but the same strip, used as a column, could not support any load.

To apply their new knowledge of stresses and to figure out the right proportions for bridge sections, David and the other students built models out of wrapping paper and glue: box-girder railroad spans and truss bridges. They tested out their models as spans between two school desks, loading them with calculated weights of books or even standing on them to show their strength. In long years ahead, when expensive wind-tunnel experiments were out of the question, David B. Steinman was to look back across his own span of life to the twelve-year-old boy's simple homemade materials and work out problems in the design and construction of history-making bridges with similar, inexpensive, ready-at-hand equipment.

In spite of David Steinman's eagerness to learn everything in the world of books, he was an all-around regular boy, although handicapped in sports by size and undernourishment. In childhood he joined the older boys in building bonfires and making snow forts, in flying kites and playing catch and spinning tops. In boyhood he was a leader in the favorite games of the time: Prisoners' Base, Cops and Robbers, and Relievo.

Walking tours were very popular, and Manhattan Island boys liked to roam in and around the boroughs of the largest city on earth. David often organized expeditions, and, as they had no money for car-fare, they learned to hitch rides on lumbering horse-drawn trucks.

Along with the other boys, David had to learn to be skillful in leaping onto the back of a moving truck while keeping out of view of the driver. If he spied the hitch-hikers, his long whip would lash out at them, and they had to be nimble in jumping off the truck and from underfoot of the other traffic.

David Steinman's boyhood was accompanied with the usual mishaps and injuries that testified to his being a normal fellow. His hand was burned quite badly by an exploding firecracker, his knee was cut severely by a spill when sliding on ice, and a fall against a stone doorstep while playing tag broke the bridge of his nose. After this last accident the doctor in the back room of the corner drug store performed a hasty stitching job, leaving a permanent scar and furrow like a frown. David was very sensitive about this mark all during his adolescent years.

Like any red-blooded youngster, he tried to imitate larger and stronger boys. One time his courage got the better of his judgment. He put a chip of wood on his shoulder, assumed a fighting stance, and gave a bigger boy the old challenge:

"Go ahead! I dare you to knock this chip off my shoulder!"

The other promptly obliged and, the next instant, David Steinman was flat on the sidewalk with a black eye and a bloody nose. He struggled to his feet, aimed wildly with his fist and went down again.

This became a history of his sports career. At every school he attended, he went out recklessly for the various teams, including football, and met the same hard knocks. Finally, one of the instructors, who was also a medical doctor, took pulse recordings of the class with a machine and then drew David aside to inform him that, with his heart, he could never be an athlete.

To a high-spirited boy starting his teens, the pronounce-
ment came like a sentence of doom, and yet in the normal course of his bridge-building career the boy who
failed in athletics was to perform feats of acrobatics on
lofty steel girders and tightrope balancing on dizzy
catwalks that would have daunted the courage and
defied the skill of many an All-American.

In his last year at grammar school, as a reward for
the fine work he had done in class and the promise he
showed as an engineer, the Commissioner of Bridges
gave David B. Steinman a pass to climb up the towers
and go over the catwalks of the Williamsburg Bridge,
then under construction. Fascinated and thrilled by
this high adventure, the boy felt as if he were walking
on air.

Watchman (grimly nodding to the school reporter) :
One slip, and he would have been!

The Williamsburg Bridge when completed would
establish a new world's record for the suspension type,
edging out the Brooklyn Bridge by a few feet, and
David Steinman was all set to have the time of his life
inspecting it when one of the chief engineers crooked
a finger at him and said:

"We've got a little problem here, son. I can't spare
a man to run the errand but we need a left-handed
monkey wrench to do a particular job, and I wonder
if you'd go over to the north tower and ask the foreman
to lend us his."

Happy as a lark, David took the catwalk high over
the East River only to be told that the foreman on the
north tower already had loaned his left-handed monkey
wrench to the foreman on the south tower.

Back David went across the catwalk, and this time
he was told that the much-sought-after tool had been
loaned to the men on Pier Nine. He promptly reported

there and was given another destination, hurrying off on his errand and not seeming to notice the broad smiles that greeted his arrival at each place when he asked:

"Do you have a left-handed monkey wrench that I could borrow?"

Finally, after he had been shuttled back and forth between the towers more times than he could count and been sent to every pier, the chief engineer who had started the game took pity on him and said: "Son, this joke's gone far enough. We've been sending you on a wild goose chase. Don't you know there isn't any such thing as a left-handed monkey wrench?"

"Yes, sir, I know," David said, smiling broadly. "I knew from the start that there's no such tool. But I figured I might get to stay longer and see more of the bridge if I pretended to hunt for one."

"You'll do, son," the engineer said after a startled pause. "I've watched you climbing around the bridge like a human fly. That takes heart." He clapped David on the shoulder. "And now I see you've got a head to match!"

But the man who hired David Steinman the summer he graduated from grammar school came to have a different idea about the young man's brains. Boss of a ladies' garment factory, he made David his bookkeeper and shipping clerk, gave him several raises in salary, and was thunderstruck to find a resignation on his desk at the end of the summer.

"Quitting to go to college?" he said incredulously. "What can more studying get you? You've already got a good job, a great future. Stick with us and I guarantee you'll be a traveling salesman making thousands of dollars a year."

When David Steinman turned down this golden

promise in favor of the vague possibility of getting through college and becoming a bridgebuilder, the boss of the ladies' garment factory was frankly disgusted.

"Suit yourself," he shrugged. "I guess there's no use trying to pound sense into young people's heads these days." He was muttering in his beard as David went out the door. "The makings of a fine traveling salesman, so he wants to be a bridge-builder yet. Pipe dreams!"

Eight

Egghead in Knickerbockers

Young men dream castles in the air,
Canals and bridges everywhere:
Grown old they call all dreamers fools,
And build neat sheds for garden tools.
                                    Capt. Ringgold

THE SCHOOL REPORTER kept glancing from the bridge
approach to the Mackinaw City area below where the
touring car with the shamrock doors was parked. "Isn't it
getting to be about time for us to ride across the Long
Crossing in your historic vehicle?" he inquired with due
care.

"Hold your horses, son," the weathered old Great
Lakes captain advised. "The car'll keep. It's been
keeping a good many years, just for this chance to haul
you over the Straits dryshod." He chuckled. "Tell me
something. What's an Egghead in your language?"

"Well, an Egghead is somebody smarter than the rest
of the class and who spends a lot of time studying. If
you don't like him, you call him a square or a longhair.
If you don't care about him one way or another, you
call him a bookworm. If you like him, you call him a
quiz whiz or Joe Brains."

The Watchman tapped the end of his nose with his
pipe as a signal of approval. "Yup, and we used to
make fun of Eggheads, mostly because we couldn't
understand them and didn't think they'd ever amount
to much outside of school life, until we woke up one

morning to find out they'd put together an atom bomb
that could blow up the whole world if all of us weren't
careful. Einstein was an Egghead. So is Dr. Salk whose
experiments at the University of Michigan resulted in
the vaccine that's got polio on the run. And the man
who designed this bridge was already an Egghead of the
first water when he started college, an Egghead in
knickerbockers! It must have been a sight for sore
eyes when he marched up the steps the first day, a college
man who hadn't yet grown out of the short pants that
mothers used to make their little boys wear!"

When David B. Steinman entered the City College
of New York, he was thirteen years old but he looked
even younger. He stood 4 feet 4½ inches tall, and he
weighed sixty pounds, sopping wet. He had never had
enough to eat in his life, and the strenuous exercises
he copied from muscle-building courses only seemed to
make him scrawnier. In addition to reading the *Scientific American* and an average of one thousand books a
year, he was an avid reader of physical culture maga-
zines, and he answered every advertisement that promised larger biceps and increased chest expansion. He
dreamed wistfully of becoming one of the bulging
young giants pictured in the ads, but these were pipe
dreams that never came true.

David B. Steinman attended City College for six
years, the first two years being an accelerated high school
course, and throughout the period he was affectionately
known as "the kid." Far from being jealous of the boy's
exceptional talents, his classmates treated him as a pet.
In effect, he became the class mascot, a bearer of good
luck to the "team," a symbol of success. An older student summed up the general feeling to a newcomer
in these words:

"We figure that if someone who started out in life as underprivileged as *the kid,* and who's as undersized as he is now, can get along so well in college, then there must be hope for everybody!"

Each morning, an hour before classes commenced, David Steinman's classmates got into the habit of clustering around him to get the gist of the assigned lessons. He never had any trouble solving the regular problems and he made short work of solving the trick puzzlers such as the one that had just swept the country and driven the average man crazy trying to figure out the answer:

"Mary is twenty-four years old. She is twice as old as Ann was when Mary was as old as Ann is now. How old is Ann now? A says the answer is sixteen. B says it is twelve. Which is correct?"

David Steinman never had difficulties with these mathematical problems, but he ran into serious trouble in another direction. In those days they had the demerit system at the College, brought there from West Point by the president. Bothered by crowded and noisy classrooms, the instructors handed out demerits freely with an eye to cutting out undesirable students. For instance, there were a thousand who started in Steinman's class but only 140 of them survived to graduate.

Under the demerit system, the older boys knew enough to watch the instructor and to cover up a whisper or a smile, but "the kid" was so naive that he had piled up 81 demerits almost before he knew it — and a total of 100 demerits meant expulsion.

One morning an instructor who happened to be in a very bad mood saw young David smile at a neighbor's whispered joke, and called out:

"Head of Section, demerit Steinman for Continued Gross Impertinence!"

It was the voice of doom. The charge carried a penalty of twenty more demerits, making a total of 101, automatic dismissal.

He was expelled from college.

It meant the end of "the kid's" education, the black death of all his hopes and ambitions. He had to turn in his textbooks and his name was stricken from the rolls. But with grim despair he continued attending classes. Finally, one red-letter day, he was called down to the president's office.

"What shall we do with this young man?" the college head asked, turning to his secretary.

"I think we can give him another chance, sir."

With such a weight removed, young David Steinman felt as light as a weather balloon ascending toward the stratosphere. Once and for all he had learned his lesson in demerits and he made up his mind to show the president that he was worthy of the second chance given him.

Like many of his classmates, he walked over a mile each way in going to school. His allowance was pitifully small and he saved part of his lunch money to pay his dues in a literary society. One night he was going to one of the meetings when a hungry man stopped him and begged for enough money to buy food. The boy took him into a restaurant and gave the proprietor twenty-five cents — all he had — to serve the man a meal, so he had to tighten his own belt at lunch time for several days afterwards.

Watchman (gesturing his pipe at the School Reporter): You might call that a sentimental gesture typical of young people like yourself, the kind of open-handedness that a lot of adolescents change into a tight fist on the rough and dream-shattered road to manhood, but Steinman's hand always remained open. You'll notice, however, that he wasn't just a soft touch. He had enough head on his shoulders to march the man into a restaurant and see that he got a good meal, instead of handing him the money and giving him a chance to spend it on liquid refreshment the way Steve Brodie would have done.

Reporter (clearing his throat very loud as a hint): Sir, I don't suppose you'd have another bottle of that raspberry shrub around?

Watchman (kicking the thermos pail until the bottles clink inside): *Talking*'s supposed to make a man dry. I never heard of such a thirsty *listener*. Stand by for a rescue, son, we'll tow you out of drydock!

All the courses at college were what boys call a snap or a breeze, as far as young Egghead Steinman was concerned. Even the course in logic seemed absurdly simple to him. Everything in the book was obvious. At the final examinations, with three hours allowed, he turned in his paper during the first half hour. The instructor called him back.

"Don't give up, Steinman," he said with sympathy. "Stick it out. There's always the chance of a passing grade if you don't quit."

"I'm not quitting, sir," the Egghead replied. "I've completed all the answers."

He scored 100 percent in the test, which, as a young golfing classmate jokingly remarked, was "Steinman's par for the course!" Throughout his college years he walked off with most of the prizes, although there was an incident in his junior year that threatened his class standing.

One day as he was working out an assigned problem

at the blackboard, the young Egghead noticed that a classmate named Noska was having trouble at the next blackboard, so he scribbled some equations on his own board to help him. The instructor noticed Noska copying Steinman's equations, called Noska to his seat, and marked him zero.

Steinman thought the situation over. If Noska's record kept that zero he would flunk the course, which would be a disaster for him, but if Steinman took a zero it meant no more than losing the Mathematics Prize for the year. So, at the end of the period, he went up to the instructor and explained:

"It was all my fault, sir. If I hadn't written down the equations to help Noska, he wouldn't have copied them. I'm the one who should get the zero."

The Egghead in Knickerbockers pleaded so hard for his friend that the instructor was put on the spot. Unwilling to see his top student lose the Mathematics Prize, he solved the problem by excusing both boys, and Noska's college career was saved. The story spread, and "the kid's" popularity grew even more. He was elected vice president of the junior class.

It was in this same school year that a great event took place in his personal life. The summer before, his sister, who had graduated from Hunter College and gone into teaching, treated him to a three-week stay at the University Settlement's fresh-air camp for boys on the Hudson River.

This was the city boy's first real introduction to the country. He was thrilled by farms, cornfields, cows, swimming holes, mountains. He learned to row a boat, and, in doing so, learned another standard item in a boy's education — how to "catch a crab." He taught himself to dog-paddle in a creek, and then struck out more skillfully into the Hudson River.

The fresh-air boys took hikes to such historic and scenic places as West Point and Bear Mountain. They sang camp songs as they marched along the country roads. They slept in tents and heard wild noises in the night. With the young Egghead scrambling far ahead of the pack, they climbed to the top of Anthony's Nose, famed in the stories of Washington Irving.

Here, twelve hundred feet up in the Highlands of the Catskills, with the wet touch of clouds on his cheeks, the bridge-builder of the future could look down on the kind of scene that would inspire and challenge him to carry out his lifework of erecting *Highways Over Broad Waters*. Far below, the blue river raced through a rocky strait and a perpetual gale seemed to storm against the trees clinging to the rugged shores. It was a place to build a bridge, and in such places the suspension spans of a day-dreaming boy were destined to be hung.

But a more immediate effect of the fresh-air adventure was the improvement in David Steinman's physique. The healthy outdoor life and improvement in diet did him worlds of good. It was typical of the Egghead to make a study of camp nutrition and then return home to teach his mother a more wholesome and appetizing system of meals, with milk and cereal and eggs for breakfast, and with hot soups and meaty stews at the other meals, instead of coffee and rolls in the morning, followed at lunch and supper by cabbage, cold delicatessen, cucumbers, and pickles. This radical change in diet brought the boy a phenomenal improvement, and his increase in measurements would have made impressive testimonials for any of the muscle-building systems he had studied. He shot up to 5 feet 8 inches in height and 135 pounds in weight.

Whereupon the great event in his personal and school life took place. He shed his knickerbockers and came to college in long trousers. His classmates staged a celebration. "The Kid" had put aside the traditional garment of boyhood and had become a young man. Even the faculty cheered. No doubt the long trousers were hand-me-downs from an older brother, but nothing could dim the glory of that momentous occasion when a boy was allowed to put on his first pair of man-sized pants instead of knickerbockers.

Commencement exercises for the City College of New York Class of '06 were held at Carnegie Hall. The Egg-head, graduated from knickerbockers, walked up the aisle to receive honor after honor — the Gold Medal in Applied Mathematics, the Memorial Prize for personal qualities and general distinction, the Debating Award, the Gold Medal for the highest scholastic standing in the College. He also was class valedictorian. The president smilingly apologized to the audience for calling him up to the platform so many times.

The boy who had been expelled from college had proven worthy of the trust and the second chance that the president had allowed him.

But in the hour of his triumphs, the young Egghead was full of doubts and despair. He wanted to go on with his education and enter Columbia University, but he had no money. His dream to become an engineer seemed to have reached an end. He would have to go to work, perhaps lose his momentum and desire in the workaday world where dollars, not dreams, set the standards of value.

In the darkest hour before dawn, the top man in the science department tapped the Egghead's shoulder. "I have some good news for you, Steinman. You'll be able to continue right on into Columbia for your engineering studies. You've been awarded a three-year teaching fellowship here in applied mechanics. Congratulations and good luck!"

So the road was paved for the young Egghead's university education, and another milestone was reached in David B. Steinman's goal of putting ferryboats out of business by building *Highways Over Broad Waters*.

Nine

Daring Young Man on the High Trapeze

As meteors burned before his eyes in wonder
The small boy thought it not at all absurd
To fling him starward and to ride the thunder
And take alive the uncapturable bird.

D. B. Steinman

"STOP MAKING EYES at my Tin Lizzie and pay attention to your notebook," the Watchman on Mackinac Bridge told the School Reporter, "while I tell you about the time the builder of the Long Crossing got pinched for speeding aboard a horse named Bill."

As a teacher at the City College of New York and a student at Columbia University, young David B. Steinman had to shuttle back and forth on the subway between classes at the two schools. They were two stations apart, with a steep climb at either end, and he had to sprint to make the trip in the ten minutes between classes. Generally he arrived a few minutes late, breathless, his heart pounding like the motor of the famous "one lung" Cadillac car of 1902, a fiery dragon that still frightened horses on city streets.

During the young student's first week at Columbia, he was called into the office of the head of the physics department. "Your fame has preceded you, my boy," the professor said, smiling. "I have the honor to offer you a teaching fellowship in physics."

The fine position would have meant an end to the hectic racing between the college and the university but, after one glance at the schedule outlined, David Steinman shook his head. "I'm sorry, sir, but I'll have to decline the honor. If I followed this schedule, I'd have to give up my engineering studies."

"So what's wrong with becoming a physicist, like Robert Millikan, or Einstein?"

"Nothing, sir, except that I want to become an engineer. I'm going to be a bridge-builder. Excuse me, sir, I *must* turn down your kind offer."

Not even after his bad accident in the university gymnasium did he regret turning down the chance that would have made life so much easier for him at Columbia. The accident came as a result of his boyish interest in body-building exercises. He spent every hour he could spare in the gym, doing "stretching" exercises on the various pieces of apparatus. He especially liked to work out on the rings, trapeze, and horizontal ladder.

Never fated to be a varsity athlete but never daunted from trying, the would-be acrobat became too eager. He lost his grip at the top rung of the horizontal ladder and fell to the unpadded gym floor, thirty feet below.

Lucky to be alive, young David Steinman went home, holding a broken left wrist. A doctor near the house set the break without looking at it through x-rays. When the break healed, the wrist was crooked and crippled. Steinman could not turn a door knob.

But the boy who had given his last twenty-five cents to feed a hungry man now met kindness himself. Given a letter to a famous surgeon, he had visions of working the rest of his life to pay the bill. The surgeon performed a marvelous operation, cutting out a wedge of bone and resetting the break in a plaster cast. His fee as a professional courtesy to a rising young engineer was five dollars, the cost of the x-ray.

On account of the accident, Steinman's arm was in
a sling for months during his first year at Columbia, and
he presented quite a spectacle making his wild dash back
to class after a teaching assignment at City College.
Fellow students joshed him, calling out:

"There goes Steinman, like a trained seal with a
busted flipper."

As part of his university training, Steinman spent the
summer of his sophomore year at Camp Columbia, Bantam Lake, Connecticut, to gain practical field work in
surveying and mapping. Not all engineering students
were dedicated to their careers, he had good reason to
notice. A fellow classmate, one of the wealthy Gould
family, would wander around the grounds or pose on
the steps of the dormitory, coaxing a "football" moustache, while his valet did the surveys for him. Elected
class treasurer, this son of fortune, unable to humble
himself to collect any dues, paid them for the entire class.

Reporter (pencil poised over notepad) : Sir, what's a
football moustache?

Watchman (chuckling): That's an old one, son.
Eleven on each side!

At Bantam Lake, young David Steinman went swimming, rowing, canoeing, and sailing. There were one
thousand acres to Camp Columbia, mostly wilderness,
and the students went around practically naked, winding
up their stay as bronzed as Mohawk savages. The
sports-minded Egghead needed all the stored-up health
he could get because, with one diploma already on his
wall, he was taking enough courses to earn three more
at the same time.

There was one incident in his sophomore year that
Steinman never forgot. Professor Burr, a member of
the Board of Engineers on the construction of the Pana-

ma Canal and a consultant to the New York City Department of Bridges, entered the lecture hall, tense and solemn.

"Gentlemen," he said, "mark the date well. I have just received a telegram bearing the tragic news that the Quebec Bridge, the world's largest, has collapsed while under construction. Eighty-two bridge men were carried down with the tangled mass of wreckage."

The news of the disaster made a lasting impression on Steinman. He studied the report that said the vast structure crumpled "like ice pillars whose ends were rapidly melting away." He studied the reports on other bridge catastrophes, and he continued these studies long after graduation. They were to prove of priceless value to him and to the entire engineering profession in time to come.

In his junior year at Columbia, the Egghead was translating some German textbooks for study purposes, writing down the English as he went along, when all of a sudden he had the idea that a publisher might be found to make his English translation into a book. Two publishers were found, two books printed.

His writing career well launched, young David Steinman began planning his graduation thesis for the Civil Engineering degree, choosing as his subject "The Design of the Henry Hudson Memorial Bridge as a Steel Arch." He had made up his mind to be an artist in steel, and his student dream was to come true many years later when his own engineering firm received the contract to build the Henry Hudson Bridge according to the design of his graduation thesis.

He received two degrees at one commencement, becoming a Civil Engineer and a Master of Arts at the same time. He had earned so many extra credits that

one more year would give him a Ph.D., and so he took
Civil Service Tests to land a summer job, getting his
first real engineering experience on the design of the
elevated tracks and station at Surf Avenue on Coney
Island. With the money he earned he was able to
enroll at Columbia for his Doctorate, choosing engineering as his major and "Long Span Bridges and Foundations" as his special course.

He was a class of *one* student. Professor Burr took
ten minutes to outline the course of study. His instructions were:

"Read everything you can find, in English, French,
and German, on the subject. At the end of the school
year, report back to me on your completed studies and
thesis. Good luck, young man!"

While Steinman was working on his fourth degree,
the Manhattan Bridge was completed across the East
River, giving New York City the three greatest suspension bridges in the world. It was no wonder that the
thesis for his Doctorate featured suspension bridges and
that the influence carried over into his career. He always favored the suspension type, as both the safest
and most artistic.

Professor Burr gave the Egghead another perfect score
on his thesis, but, in order to meet all requirements for
the Ph.D., he had to get the paper printed and so he
accepted another Civil Service appointment for the
summer, this time as an engineering inspector on the
construction of the Catskill Aqueduct, a project designed
to bring 400 million gallons of water per day to the
thirsty City of New York.

As he worked on this dramatic engineering achieve-
ment, another part of young David Steinman's many-
sided nature felt the wild and wonderful poetry of the

setting, saw Rip Van Winkle and the Headless Horseman in the mountaintop mists, heard in every rumbling thunder-storm the ghostly crew of Hendrick Hudson rolling their nine-pin balls across the echoing Catskills.

Toward the end of the summer, he answered an ad for an instructor in Civil Engineering at the University of Idaho and his credentials were considered the best of seventy-two applicants. Whereupon he turned his face westward, the direction in which, at the height of his powers, he was destined to build his proudest bridge.

Reporter (with boyish pride) : The Long Crossing at the Straits of Mackinac!

Watchman (mildly) : This bridge doesn't need any bragging, son. Seeing's believing!

Young David Steinman boarded a west-bound train with a trunk, a suitcase, and a crate of books. Like most Easterners he expected to see nothing but frontier settlements beyond the Hudson River. His thoughts pictured a dime-novel Wild West, complete with painted Indians and shaggy-maned buffalo, cowboys and cattle rustlers. The civilized appearance of Chicago was a great disappointment to him. Stopping off there he took a boat ride out into Lake Michigan. Almost four hundred miles up the cucumber-shaped lake, farther than any eye could see but visible to any dreamer, were the brawling Straits of Mackinac.

Arrived at Moscow, the small town where the University of Idaho was located, the new college instructor found himself in surroundings that looked more like his paperback impressions of the West. There was a mountain six thousand feet tall right outside his boarding house window. Big game — elk, antelope, bear, mountain goats — roamed the nearby slopes. While teaching a surveying class for the first time, he spotted twenty forest fires, and students showed up for instruction burned and bandaged from fighting them.

Cowpunchers were the lords of the earth. A few trail-blazing Model-T touring cars with plucky brass radiators could be seen adventuring across the rugged hills with a reckless lumberjack or prospector at the throttle, but most of Idaho relied on the horse for transportation, and young Steinman wasted no time in joining the crowd. From the geology professor he bought a complete outfit with a western saddle and a five-gaited white cavalry stallion named Bill.

Although modest about his Egghead accomplishments, David Steinman shared every young man's yearning to "shine" in things that he could not do. His dreams featured an admiring crowd shouting, "There goes Steinman riding like a Comanche!" but in the cold light of day his knees started to shake.

After cautious experiments behind the barn, he ventured out for his first ride in public, only to find the sidewalks lined with smiling members of the faculty, with a few grinning students peeking out of the crowd here and there. But he thought he was running the gauntlet pretty well until a member of his surveying class advised him in a loud whisper:

"Professor, out West we hold both reins in one hand!"

But no rider aboard Bill could remain a tenderfoot for long. He showed his master how to jump hedges and fences, how to gallop at breakneck speed across country. They became inseparable friends. Every morning they galloped through town to the university where, in front of his classroom, Steinman would drop the reins and leave Bill to wait for him on the campus.

One day a woman telephoned the president of the University of Idaho, complaining: "There's a college

boy on a white horse keeps galloping across our fields like crazy. Can't you learn them to settle down and study 'stead of gallivantin'?"

A more serious complaint was made one morning several days later. The town constable came rapping at the young professor's classroom door. "Come along to the courthouse," he said officially. "Judge wants to see you!"

While the engineering students wondered at the sight of their teacher being arrested and marched off to face the law, Steinman himself was full of anxious wonder. Had he broken a western law without knowing it? What charge could they possibly have against him? Did this mean jail?

At the court house the judge thumbed through several bulky volumes and finally located an old city ordinance declaring it a misdemeanor to ride a horse faster than eight miles an hour on the city streets. He turned to the constable and said: "Officer, will you swear that the professor was going over eight miles an hour?"

"Yes, your honor. I will swear he was going over *twenty-eight* miles an hour!"

The judge rapped his gavel. "That official testimonial about the speed of your horse ought to be worth the three-dollar fine and the five dollar court costs," he told the young defendant. "Everybody will envy you for having a horse that fast!"

A Spokane, Washington, newspaper picked up the story and for weeks afterwards members of the faculty and student body delighted in playing out a little drama whenever they came across young David Steinman. They would pull out the newspaper and shake their heads gravely as they stared at the incriminating headline:

IDAHO PROFESSOR FINED FOR SPEEDING

In all his four years of teaching at the western university, Steinman never was allowed to forget the incident, because every new engineering student had to be told the old story, but the young instructor never minded that joke. It was a matter of pride to him, and a compliment to his friend Bill, that he had a police record of having the fastest horse in the West.

Ten

Camp Laff-a-Lot Boy Scout Bridge

The smaller you are,
The farther it is
To the sun or a star;
But, if you dream hard enough,
NOTHING's *too far.*

Tiny Tim Pine

"IF BILL COULD really gallop twenty-eight miles an hour," said the School Reporter, "could he have beaten your Model T touring car across Mackinac Bridge in a race?"

"Stop hinting," the Watchman said with a wink. "You'll get that ride quick enough, and you'd better get a pair of built-in shock absorbers first!"

At the age of twenty-three, David B. Steinman became the youngest college professor in America. Some of his engineering students at the University of Idaho were older than he, and most of them looked older. He was popular not only on the campus but also in the town because of the boyish way he acted.

One afternoon as he came galloping home from his classroom on Bill, a snowball hit him. He singled out the culprit in a group of boys and, without dismounting, chased him across the sidewalk into a front yard. There he jumped from the saddle and, in great good humor, washed the boy's face with snow. This forthright retaliation, without pulling his authority as a professor, won him the respect and liking of all the boys.

Some time later a delegation of these boys called on David Steinman. They wanted to form a troop of Boy Scouts, and they had voted to ask him to be their Scoutmaster. The Boy Scout movement had just started in the United States, and the present group represented the first troop in Idaho.

Steinman agreed to take charge and located a tent where they could hold meetings. He got a Boy Scout Manual, studied it, and initiated the youngsters. They all ordered uniforms and equipment from Boy Scout headquarters in New York and they were proud as generals when they could march around in full regalia, their young Scoutmaster included. He started with fifteen boys and before long counted seventy-two in the troop, so he trained two assistant Scoutmasters.

Summer camp was the big project each year, and the first camping site was on Moscow Mountain where Scoutmaster Steinman persuaded friends on the faculty to make their log cabin available. The boys supplied their own tents, blankets, canteens, and mess-kits. Town merchants donated provisions. The nine car-owners in Moscow furnished transportation.

It was a question who had the most fun at this first camp, the Boy Scouts or their boyish leader. He organized nature study, handcraft, games, Boy Scout contests. Now and then he had to smile to himself at the thought that a tenderfoot from Manhattan was teaching these Western boys camping and woodcraft. He even instructed them in camp cooking, but his experience in the fresh-air camps along the Hudson River had given him a solid background in outdoor living.

There were few idle moments for Scoutmaster or Scouts. They built signal towers and practiced wig-wagging. They built a dam and deepened the small brook to make a swimming hole. On Sundays, when parents came to visit, the boys entertained them with water sports, including log-rolling contests.

The next summer Steinman established a new camp for his Boy Scouts at a scenic point at the Forks of the Potlatch River. In the center of a large open clearing, they erected a sixty-foot flagpole, no small engineering feat, and then set up their circle of tents along the rim. The leader named the place "Camp Laff-a-Lot" and it lived up to its name.

The Potlatch River marked an important milestone in David Steinman's career. Here he showed the boys how to build a bridge out of logs, a cantilever bridge of original design. The span measured forty feet, but the longest logs the boys could handle were only twenty-four feet in length, so a considerable job of engineering had to be performed. At the dedication, photographs were taken of the bridge supporting the entire troop of Boy Scouts. Their young Scoutmaster beamed proudly. It was his first bridge, and — who knows? — it might lead to greater things!

The Boy Scout Bridge across the Potlatch River, a remarkable construction built without a nail, caused quite a stir around the country. The story and the picture of the bridge jammed with Boy Scouts appeared in *Engineering News* and various newspapers across the nation.

But, in the months that followed, the proud builder of the bridge slowly lost his naturally cheerful outlook on life. He wrote to Gustav Lindenthal, the dean of American bridge-builders, and confided to the expert his ambition to specialize in long-span bridges. Lindenthal replied in a discouraging way, stating that no more big bridges would ever be built because the price of steel had gone up too high.

The old bridge-builder's statement was about as

accurate as another carefully considered verdict of the day — that the automobile was merely a passing fad — but, on top of other things, it put young David Steinman in the lowest mood of his life.

On June 11, friends gave him a picnic party to cheer him up and celebrate his birthday, but it was no use. He was miserably homesick and lonesome, but something else bothered him most of all. He was troubled with the sense of failure that every gifted youth has brooded upon through the ages.

Here he was, in his twenties, half of his life gone, and nothing accomplished!

To be sure he had four college degrees to his credit, he was a full professor, and he was entitled to be addressed as Dr. Steinman, but the only work of construction he could point to was a Boy Scout bridge made of logs in the wilds of Idaho.

But he finally worked his own way out of despair. "Listen," he told himself sternly, "if you dream hard enough, and then go out and *do* something about it, nothing's impossible."

He sat down and wrote another letter to Lindenthal, stated that he was available for any bridge-building job, however small.

Back came a reply by return mail:

"Report at once in New York to assist me on design and construction of two of world's greatest bridges."

Young David Steinman let out a yell and sailed his hat almost as high as timberline on Moscow Mountain.

Eleven

Dropping Pebbles Down Smoke Stacks

So nigh is grandeur to our dust,
So near is God to man,
When Duty whispers low, "Thou must,"
The youth replies, "I can."

Emerson

LOLLING BACK in the captain's chair with a wicked look in his eye, the Watchman on Mackinac Bridge shot a double-barreled question at his young interviewer. "Any good school reporter ought to be able to answer me this," he said with a challenge in his voice. "Who wrote *You Know Me, Al* and *Alibi Ike* and made Yankee manager Casey Stengel one of the real-life characters in his baseball stories, and, if you know so much, what was the name of his home town?"

"Ring Lardner," shot back the School Reporter in a triumphant tone, "and his home town was Niles, Michigan, and he studied engineering but he flunked all the courses, so he got a job as a sports reporter on a Chicago newspaper—"

"That's plenty," the Watchman said, holding up his hand in surrender and approval. "You know the writing business, son. What I'm driving at is that Ring Lardner's son went to New York and became a reporter himself. About the time Dr. Steinman was designing this Mackinac Bridge here, he wrote an article for *Look* Magazine called 'John Lardner's New York, Love and

Adventure on All the Bridges, While Cats Sit in Windows Snarling at Pigeons.' "

"That's an awfully long title," the School Reporter said with professional criticism. "We wouldn't use that long a title on our school paper."

"Hmmmm." The old sailor's deepwater blue eyes twinkled. "Well, anyway, John Lardner reported that a youth proposed to a girl on the Williamsburg Bridge, and the girl said no. The youth climbed on a girder and threatened to jump. The girl ran to a telephone to call the police and said there was a man trying to jump off the George Washington Bridge. She had the wrong bridge by ten miles, but the cops noted the location of the call and went to the right bridge and saved the youth. If they'd gone to the George Washington Bridge, Lardner reported, they'd have found love and adventure there too, it's such a wonderful town."

"It sure must be a wonderful place for bridges," the School Reporter admitted.

"And the most wonderful town in the world for a boy to be born and raised in if he's going to be a bridge-builder," the Watchman declared. "Just imagine David Steinman being born within sight of the Brooklyn Bridge, and then being able to watch the Williamsburg and Manhattan and the Queensborough bridges under construction while he grew up and went to school, and then being called back from a Boy Scout bridge in Idaho to build his first real bridge right in his own home town. That's not luck, son, that's a guiding Providence!"

If anyone had stopped the wiry figure of David Steinman on the street in the days after his return to New York and demanded, "Who are you, young man?" he would have drawn himself up proudly to his full height of five feet eight inches and replied:

"Special Assistant to Gustav Lindenthal, Consulting

Engineer and Architect. My job is to serve as right-hand man to the Dean of American bridge engineers in the design and construction of two new record-breaking spans — the Hell Gate Arch Bridge over the East River here in New York, and the Sciotoville Bridge over the Ohio River between Ohio and Kentucky. Now, sir, if you'll excuse me, I've got work to do!"

In serving as Lindenthal's right-hand man, young Steinman had to make trips to steel plants in Pennsylvania, to cement mills in Indiana, and to the Sciotoville Bridge site in Ohio, but it was at the Hell Gate Arch Bridge site that he found his greatest thrill in being on the job. Here the builders had located the perfect setting for a bridge.

The East River was really a strait flowing between New York and Brooklyn, connecting the harbor with Long Island Sound which was twenty miles outside the famed "Hell Gate." This passage, once the terror of mariners, carried the greater part of the Hudson River tidal current, and the tremendous rush of water through the rocky gorge had prompted the early Dutch to name the place *hellegat* or *hoilgat,* meaning either *beautiful* or *whirlpool* channel, which the American settlers had taken into their own language as Hell Gate.

In this haunted setting of shipwrecks and skyscrapers, on his first professional engineering engagement, David B. Steinman helped create one of the world's most famous and monumental bridges. From the start he showed that he was not going to be any mere desk engineer, drawing blueprints and giving orders. He was *on* the job, at every stage of construction, in all kinds of weather.

With a heavy box of instruments slung on his back, he climbed up icy steel ladders, went hand over hand up dangling ropes, squeezed through twenty-inch manholes into the interior of the steel members, and then crawled through these members, from section to section, making his stress measurements. He knew every rivet in the structure, and there were 1 million 174 thousand of them. He had a speaking acquaintance with the sea gulls that soared where he climbed!

The boy who had been turned down for football and who had fallen from a gym ladder proved as daring and catfooted as a circus highwire performer in going through his everyday duties on the bridge. He had to climb to a height of 350 feet, the top 200 feet on exposed steel ladders, in all kinds of weather, to reach the tops of the backstay towers.

He felt at home at the top of the arch and often took his lunch box up there after the noon whistle blew. He was still very much of a boy at heart, and his actions sometimes proved it.

During one lunch period a foreman down below beckoned to some of the other bridge workers and then pointed up to the top of the bridge, shaking his head in wonder. "Look at the boss!"

There sat David B. Steinman, the eminent engineer, with his feet dangling over the sheer edge of nothing. He was sitting on the top chord at the mid-span end of the half-arch, leaning over and trying to drop pebbles into the smoke stacks of ships passing through Hell Gate three hundred feet below him.

"Four college degrees," one of the bridge workers muttered, "and he sits up there with no more thought of danger than a kid on a curbstone playing with toy boats in a gutter!"

"If he's any sample of a bookworm," the foreman said, "there ought to be more bookworms in this business. It's a pleasure working under a boss like him, and, boys," he went on with his eyes aloft in admiration, "I mean, *under!*"

Twelve

Rocket Cars on the Chicago Skyride

Around the bridge in afterglow
The city's lights like fireflies gleam
And eyes look up to see the span —
A poem stretched across the stream.

Steinman

"BRIDGEMEN are about as unsissified a crew as you'll find," the Watchman said, sucking on his empty pipe, "but, if a fortune teller had come along and told those workers on the Hell Gate Arch that their young boss would build more bridges that were called poems and write more poems about bridges than any man in history, I bet they'd all have tried to write poetry, figuring it must be a two-fisted pastime for rugged characters."

The School reporter poised his pencil over the notepad. "Did Dr. Steinman write any poems when he was a boy?"

"Not that I know of, son. The poetry in words came later, after he had *written*, you might say, more than four hundred epic poems in stone and steel, written them against the skyline on five continents, in handwriting strong enough to last a thousand years."

For a while, after the Hell Gate Arch and Sciotoville projects were finished, young David Steinman wondered if he would ever get a chance to build more bridges. Dr. Lindenthal had retired and his "boy wonder" of the engineering world was thrown out of work. He had started at the top of his profession, and he began to worry how long it might be before he hit rock bottom.

He walked the streets so much hunting a job that it reminded him of the time his father had whipped him for wasting shoe leather. Finally, after landing a few bridge-building jobs that were full of ups and downs, he decided that the best way to make sure of a good steady job was to go into business for himself. So he founded his own engineering firm by renting desk-space in the small office of an older engineer and advertising himself in neat printed announcements sent to engineering firms and architects:

> DAVID B. STEINMAN, CONSULTING ENGINEER. SERVICES AVAILABLE IN STRESS ANALYSIS, ENGINEERING COMPUTATIONS, STRUCTURAL DESIGN, ETC.

It was a time of world-wide depression. There were no replies to the new firm's mailing campaign. The president sat at his rented desk and looked very busy and important if anyone came in the door, but the visitors were all for the older engineer. Weeks passed. Steinman and Company took in no money.

On St. Patrick's Day he was held up by the annual parade on Fifth Avenue. Buried in gloom, he had to watch bands playing, flags flying, crowds cheering. Everybody in the world seemed to have something to celebrate about, except him.

Watchman (flourishing the long-stemmed white-clay Irish pipe decorated with the tiny green shamrocks and golden harp on the bowl): That sad St. Patrick's Day made a deep impression on Dr. Steinman. You know, he started the custom of adding beauty to bridges by painting them a bright color instead of black or battleship gray. And, judging by the bridges that he's built and painted, any color is okay with him — as long as it's some shade of green!

Reporter (filling his eyes with the Long Crossing's coat of paint) : You mean that, just because he had nothing to celebrate when he was held up by the St. Patrick's Day parade, he's been celebrating the "wearing of the green" ever since with each new bridge?

Watchman: Yup, a kind of sign to the world that defeat can be turned into victory. (Chuckling): You can't get away from the influence of the Irish in this story, son, not if you go all the way back to the Killarney Mountains that brewed the steel that Dr. Steinman painted green because he felt so blue one grand St. Patrick's Day!

Reporter: But what about the towers? He had them painted ivory.

Watchman: That's another kind of sign of how come this bridge was built, son. Don't ivory towers always stand for Eggheads who are dreamers?

Shortly after David B. Steinman's dismal St. Patrick's Day, word began to get around the various offices that there was a bright young engineer in the building who could solve just about any kind of problem simply by fooling around with his slide-rule. Neighboring office-workers dropped in for free consultations that were cheerfully given by the president of the penniless engineering firm. The first stroke of business came when Steinman's quick slide rule solved a knotty technical problem in a few minutes and the grateful person forced a five dollar bill into his hand. This marked the only money the new firm had earned in several months of existence, and it seemed to change Steinman and Company's luck.

Dr. Lindenthal started to send clients to his favorite

young engineer. A turning point came when a railroad company hired Steinman to inspect their bridges. The clients had mentioned five bridges, and a price of $450 had been agreed on for the job, but when the consulting engineer arrived at the scene, which lay roughly between New York's Finger Lakes and Lake Chautauqua, he found there were forty-five bridges saddled out over one hundred miles of the railroad line.

Steinman conscientiously spent several days going over this straggling railroad foot by foot. He carefully studied each bridge, climbing down ravines to examine the foundations and the masonry abutments, clambering over the steelwork to check the amount of rusting, and testing the rivets with a rivet-hammer.

After this field work, he spent weeks in his desk-room office, going over blueprints and calculating the stresses. Then he wrote his report on the forty-five bridges, all for the original fee, which added up to ten dollars a bridge, a far cry from the three or four million dollars a bridge he would be getting in a few years. His report stated his findings in blunt language: Most of the bridges needed strengthening, some of them were in a dangerous condition.

The officials of the railroad line read Steinman's report with uneasy eyes. Times were hard and money was tight. Funds could not be spared for the needed repairs, they decided, and so the report was filed away.

Then Providence took a hand, as it did so many times during Steinman's career. One by one, during the next few months, abutments started caving in and spans collapsing on the bridges Steinman had condemned. He received a hurried wire:

COME AT ONCE AND MAKE BRIDGES SAFE. RETAINING FEE $2500.

At last Steinman was back on the map where bridges were concerned. This job, and the fine work he did on it, established him as a top-flight consulting engineer. His practice grew as if a magic seed had been planted. He moved into a large new office, and bridge clients seemed to elbow one another aside in their rush to get through the door.

Life went into high gear for young David B. Steinman. He saw a pretty girl on a trolley car one Sunday, fell in love at first sight, married her after a whirlwind court-ship, and they settled down to raise a family of Eggheads.

At the office he took in a partner to help him handle the growing business of the firm and together, until the partner's death, they became associated as consulting engineers on the construction of most of the well-known long-spans in America, including the George Washing-ton Bridge, the Ambassador Bridge at Detroit, the San Francisco Transbay Bridge, and the Triborough Bridge in New York.

Watchman (chuckling): It always tickled Dr. Stein-man in later years that Joseph B. Strauss who built the Golden Gate Bridge, second only to Long Mack, couldn't play football any better than himself. When he went out for the team at the University of Cincin-nati, the other players just laughed at the idea of little Joe Strauss going out for such a rugged sport. But little Joe went on to score quite a touchdown across San Francisco Bay, and there are plenty of All-Americans who'd head for the locker room rather than climb out on his Golden Gate Bridge!

Reporter (writing his own shorthand): *N.G. for U. C. team, J. S. scores T. D. at S. F.*

Unlike the ordinary consulting engineer, young David Steinman set a vigorous example for his office staff, get-ting away from his desk and drafting board to travel across country, visiting and studying various bridge sites, scrambling down river banks and canyons at the risk of his neck. In the space of one year he made reports and designs for bridges over the Ohio, Mississippi, Delaware, Missouri, and St. Lawrence rivers in the eastern half of North America, then skipped as far out west as the Snake River in Idaho, and finally made a long leap beyond to Sydney Harbour, Australia.

In another twelve-month period, Steinman bridge projects ranged from Grand' Mere, Quebec, to the Thousand Islands to Omaha, Nebraska, and from the New York Narrows to Astoria, Oregon, and Tacoma, Washington.

The grand total of David B. Steinman bridges, counting three new international bridges over the St. Lawrence Seaway, a railroad bridge over the Indus River in Pakistan, the intercontinental Bosporus Bridge from Asia to Europe, and the Iraq Bridge across the Tigris River, all currently underway, had reached the incredible total by Mackinac Bridge's first birthday of 440 monumental structures scattered around the world on every continent but Africa. However, across the years there were special bridge jobs that the onetime newsboy at Brooklyn Bridge singled out for one reason or another.

Steinman had a glad eye for the Florianapolis Bridge in Brazil, largest and most famous in South America. Perhaps its Irish tieup as well as its technical perfection appealed to him. The name Brazil appeared on maps in the Middle Ages and may be traced back to the days of Saint Brendan the Sailor. Irish lore told of an island in the Atlantic Ocean where heroes were sent as their reward after death. Early explorers from Ireland gave this place the Gaelic name of Braes-ail, meaning a blessed or fortunate isle.

Another favorite bridge picture on the walls of

Steinman's engineering office overlooking New York Harbor was a photograph of the Carquinez Strait Bridge in California, the world's first bridge designed to withstand earthquake forces. This Steinman-built bridge blazed a trail for the Golden Gate and Transbay bridges of San Francisco.

The Mount Hope Bridge over Narragansett Bay in Rhode Island, the largest bridge in New England and the one that was built to "take the island out of Rhode Island," had several reasons for being a favorite of the builder. The structure replaced an historic three-hundred-year-old ferry which had transported General Washington and General Lafayette, and the ferry was owned and operated by William H. Vanderbilt, an heir of the Commodore Vanderbilt whose Staten Island ferry had established the family fortunes.

But the Mount Hope Bridge, connecting Providence and the socially elite summer resort of Newport, had two more important claims to attention. This marked the first bridge on which Steinman used color, starting out with a light greenish tint.

Watchman (tapping the shamrocks on his pipe): In later bridges he went on from light green to verde green, jade green, apple green, foliage green, forest green, emerald green, shamrock green, kelly green, and other shades of St. Patrick's Day!

Reporter (grinning and trying to whistle "The Wearin' o' the Green" together).

Watchman: Sure, and the canal gangs of Charles T. Harvey had so much faith in the favorite color of young David B. Steinman that when Harvey's Hammer, a steam punch with three tons of fist on a thirty-foot arm, failed to break up a rock ledge in the Soo Canal, they didn't do anything but paint his invention green

— and it broke up the ledge into pieces as small as rock candy for Young Mister Big!

Reporter (sober-faced as he makes a thoughtful note) : *Soo Canal and Long Mack, 50 miles apart in space, 100 years apart in time, but close as twins in spirit.*

It was also on the Mount Hope Bridge in New England that Steinman pioneered the artistic illumination of bridges, pin-pointing the cables with light and giving them the appearance of necklaces strung with beads of gold. Inspired by this bridge, other engineers all around the globe started to copy Steinman's ideas of bright colors and night lights.

He had a warm place in his heart, and a choice spot on his office walls, for the Waldo-Hancock Bridge at Bucksport, Maine, over the Penobscot River, a white water stream rolling between wild forests and famed for its log drives in early lumberjack days. Here the enthusiastic fresh-air camp graduate learned to enjoy the hardy New England breakfasts which included steak, codfish balls, fried potatoes, and mince pie each morning to fortify a man for the day's battle with the elements.

An exciting experience kept another bridge uppermost in Steinman's memories — the St. John's Bridge at Portland, Oregon, over the Willamette River near its junction with the broad-flowing, ripple-blown Columbia. On a stormy day, a stunt pilot named Tex Rankin dared the engineer to go flying. It was a wild ride. They flew over and under and around the span. Newspapers reported that it was the first time an engineer had ever inspected a bridge from the air. Several other Steinman bridges were given the national Artistic Bridge Award, but many people have insisted on regarding the St. John's Bridge as the most beautiful bridge in the world.

The bridge that gave the boyish builder the most

fun in building and that provided the most fun for others was the Chicago Skyride built for the Century of Progress World's Fair. The most spectacular entertainment feature ever constructed, it had a span length as long as the record-breaking Ambassador Bridge across the Detroit River, and could carry as much traffic on its string of ten suspended cars, each holding thirty-six wide-eyed passengers.

With calliope music in the background, a circus barker would shout to the crowds: "Hurry, hurry, hurry, step right up and get your tickets for thrills, chills, but we hope no spills! Crane your necks to see those two towers standing like giant sentinels, seeming to guard the Hall of Science on the mainland and the Hall of Social Science across the lagoon. Those cloud-kissing towers are the sole support of the spectacular Skyride, great thrill feature of the Century of Progress. At the last World's Fair, it was the monster ferris wheel that everybody talked about and everybody rode but today, striking example of the progress of science even in thrill makers, we offer you this suspension bridge principle applied to an entertainment feature, and, folks, it's tops!

"They are higher than any building in Chicago, those two strong steel towers imbedded deep in cement. Six hundred and twenty-eight feet they rise into the skies, with observation floors atop them. If you stand in one of those observation rooms at night and look down, you gaze upon a magic city that seems to float in a vast pool of light. From the towers, great searchlights sweep the sky, the lake, and over the great city to the west, to clash with other beams of light. In the day, look down and it is a pattern of many hues, like a gigantic gay rug or a vast garden of colorful flowers. Far to the south you look upon Indiana, and to the north upon Wisconsin, to the west Illinois, and eastward across the lake you can see Michigan.

"Airplanes and dirigibles may pass, as cars do on the ground, and clouds may swirl about you. You are standing a hundred feet higher than the observation level of Washington monument. On a two-hundred-foot level the rocket cars offer you a glorious and, may-hap, spine-tingling ride across the lagoon. The towers and rocket cars can handle five thousand visitors an hour, but the whole world's here at Chicago's Century of Progress Exposition, so hurry, hurry, hurry!"

In fact, the Skyride towers were the tallest structures west of Manhattan. The electric elevators that carried sightseers to the tops were the fastest ever built. A rumor spread that on windy days the tops of the towers swayed a couple of feet; actually only a couple of inches.

The Skyride still holds the world record as the longest-span transporter bridge ever built, and its rocket cars carried 4,500,000 passengers during the two seasons of the World's Fair. The Skyride also has the distinction of being the only one of Steinman's bridges no longer standing. When the Exposition ended, the Century of Progress had to be dismantled, Skyride included. The city of Chicago soon had proof that even Steinman's temporary structures were built to endure. To wreck his thrill-maker and bring down the towers, so much high explosive had to be used that the blasts blew out shopwindows along Michigan Avenue.

After the towers of the Skyride buckled and came down, David B. Steinman walked down to the water's edge and stared across Lake Michigan. He remembered one of his last talks with Dr. Lindenthal, when he had been the older bridgebuilder's trusted lieutenant.

"Steinman, I want you to find out for me where is the

place out West where the railroad crosses by train-ferry."

"There are two such places, sir, Carquinez Strait in California and the Straits of Mackinac in Michigan."

The young engineer had secured maps and charts and studied the possibility of a bridge at each of these crossings. In due time he had put a bridge across the California water barrier. Now, staring up Lake Michigan with the ruins of his Skyride behind him, he wondered if he ever would get a chance to try to bridge the much more formidable crossing where two of the Great Lakes came brawling together through a prehistoric glacial gorge.

He wondered, but he could not know that the chance would come only after he had made a decision which would dismay his associates, shock his friends, and make him the laughing stock of his enemies.

It would be a hard decision for David B. Steinman to make, but it would change the course of bridge-building history.

Thirteen

Tin Liz and Merry Olds

Yes, it's Tin, Tin, Tin!
You exasperating puzzle Hunka Tin;
I've abused you and I've flayed you,
But by Henry Ford that made you,
You are better than a Packard — Hunka Tin.

Rudyard Kipling, Jr.

"WHAT KIND of a decision did the builder of Long Mack have to make?" the School Reporter asked, full of curiosity and impatient to make more notes on his pad.

"About the hardest kind of decision a man ever has to make," the Watchman on Mackinac Bridge replied, his teeth clenched on his pipe and speaking around it. "The kind of decision a sailing master has to make sometimes in the middle of a storm, when the safety of his vessel and the lives of all the passengers and crew are in his hands, and when he knows that the first mate and the chief engineer and every other responsible officer are dead set against his judgment and are sure he's got them all headed for destruction on the rocks."

"You mean Dr. Steinman had to make a decision that went against everybody's judgment, even the other engineers?"

"Yup. There are times, son, when a man has to get away from the crowd and think his own thoughts and and then go his own way, regardless. It's a hard and lonesome road because it's going slambang against common sense, tradition and the popular idea of what's

102

right. It's a road that's lined with smashups and fatal accidents, but once in a great while somebody gets through in spite of everything and then there's a deed to write down in the history books."

The old Lakes sailor pointed his long-stemmed pipe over the bridge approach down to the Mackinaw City parking area where the Model T touring car could be seen. "Take a good look at old Tin Liz."

Reporter (eagerly): Are we going to ride across Long Mack now?

Watchman: Pretty quick. Fasten your seat belt and put on your space helmet. (Teeth clenching on his pipe again): All joking aside, son, that antique hunk of tin you're looking at down there stands for one of the hardest and most revolutionary decisions in the history of transportation.

The first automobiles that rolled on city streets were the playthings of the rich, far beyond the average pocketbook. The hoot in which young Steinman joined — "Get a horse!" — had its share of envy as well as derision. It was when schoolboy Steinman received a pass from the New York Commissioner of Bridges to climb around the unfinished Williamsburg Bridge that the famous curved dashboard Oldsmobile made its first appearance.

Today one of the most highly prized items by antique car collectors, the curved dash Olds caught the fancy of the public as no other car on the market had been able to do. A young man from Lansing, Michigan, almost overnight became the largest manufacturer of automobiles in the world. Ransom E. Olds, his name still celebrated by one of the most popular cars on the road, also carved his initials into transportation history by building the REO car and truck.

The Oldsmobile made such a hit with the public that

Sir Thomas Lipton, the tea magnate, was soon steering
one of the curved dash contraptions through London
traffic and the Queen of Italy started romping up and
down the seven hills of Rome, past the Colosseum and
the Parthenon and entrance to the Catacombs in her
royal gold-plated Olds. Gus Edwards, the vaudeville
star, brought the car into every home and made it a
household word with his catchy tune, "In My Merry
Oldsmobile."

Meanwhile, a young man from Dearborn, Michigan,
who had gone around the country tinkering with dollar
watches before he landed a job with the Detroit Edison
Company as an engineer, was approached by his em-
ployer who said:

"Listen, Hank, if you'll stop puttering around with
that worthless invention of yours and give your full
time to our company, we'll give you a raise in salary to
forty dollars a week. What do you say?"

"What do I say?" Henry Ford echoed, laying down
his tools and taking off his overalls, "I quit!"

Instead of giving full time to the Detroit Edison
Company, he made up his mind to give full time to his
own invention, a gas engine installed in a horseless
buggy, that steered with a tiller instead of a wheel, like
a sailboat. Finally, after he had pounded and patched
and pasted all the parts together, he tried it out on the
street, and, as he reported later, discovered a little bit
to his own surprise:

"The silly thing ran!"

While young David Steinman was walking away with
all the prizes at the City College of New York, Henry
Ford built his famous racing car, the 999, named after
the locomotive that set a world speed record on the New
York Central. With cigar-chewing Barney Oldfield at
the throttle, old Number 999 broke the mile record

for automobiles as it roared and skidded over the ice of Baltimore Bay on Lake St. Clair.

In 1908 Henry Ford built his first Model T car and in the following year, while David B. Steinman was getting his degree in Civil Engineering from Columbia University, the man who turned down forty dollars a week from the Detroit Edison Company to become a billionaire made a decision of historic importance. Tired of all the new models and fancy trimmings that kept the automobile out of reach of the common man, Henry Ford petrified his associates and proclaimed the dawn of a new era in mass production and mass transportation by delivering this ultimatum:

"From now on, we are going to build only one model. That model is going to be the Model T. The chassis will be the same for all cars. And any customer can have a car painted any color he wants so long as it is black!"

The ultimatum from Detroit supplied the world with cheap transportation and sent the ubiquitous and everlasting Tin Lizzie into the most improbable corners of the globe. Millions of flivvers rabbiting across the landscape began to play their part in setting the stage for the most dramatic act of David Steinman's life. They, too, contributed their share as the builders of the Bridge.

When young Professor Steinman went West to teach engineering at the University of Idaho, the automobile revolution went into full orbit. The fabulous promoter who died broke, W. C. Durant, gathered the Olds Motor Works and other car firms into a new company called General Motors. The Lincoln Highway was on the move toward becoming a transcontinental bridge for cars and trucks. Campaigns for good roads swept the country. One appeal said:

"Just think! At the speed of fifteen miles per hour you can go from Detroit to New York in less than four days! Send five dollars to the Lincoln Highway Association, Detroit, Michigan, and this will make you a life member of the Anti-Piker Association of America."

The Idaho interlude in Steinman's life saw the installation of Charles F. Kettering's self-starter in the 1912 Cadillac, and the coming of the demountable rim, the cord tire, and the closed car in place of the unseaworthy tourings or runabouts that had to stay home or head for shelter in bad weather. The coming of the closed car gave the most ordinary American an advantage over the greatest kings and conquering generals of all time. It gave him a self-propelled room on wheels.

This perambulating room equipped with rubber tires, an accelerator, and brakes filled the motoring American with a personal pride and a sense of power utterly unknown to any man in past history. The car became his flying horse and his ivory tower, his compensation for business troubles and family quarrels, his release from tensions, his escape. No matter what happened to bother him, he could always get out on the road for awhile and *let himself go*.

During David Steinman's early manhood, America became increasingly transportation-conscious and, for most of the United States and the world in general, transportation meant one car in particular — the Model T. Will Rogers once said:

"If there had never been a Ford car, there never would have been a cheap car. You can remember when we all had it in for the rich men that come along our roads honking for us commoners to get out of the way. We was sore at them and hated the guys that was in them, but the minute that Ford built a cheap one and we was the ones that was doing the honking — that made it different.

"Hoover fed the Belgians, but Ford took them for a ride. About 103,000 people is just fixing punctures on those things every minute of every day, and 432,000 is just advising them how to fix them. There is 30,000 Ford radiators boiling over the hills of this country every minute of the day, 21,000 people just holding up the hoods and looking at the radiators, 20,000 with the same expression.

"The Ford car is the best known object in the world. You can take a Chinaman in the heart of China that don't know where his next missionary is coming from but he knows how to pour a couple of quarts of rice in the thing and it will run. An Englishman knows it like he does his teapot. A Zulu can take one apart and get enough back so it will run. There is more jokes told about it than any other thing. Henry Ford was the first man to realize that every joke sold a car and every joker bought one. He has caused more dirty dishes to be left in the sink after supper than all the leading men on the screen put together. He has broken more wrists than all the osteopaths combined. He has run over more people in one month than either Washington or Lincoln disposed of in both wars."

In his good-humored talk that made fun of the old Model T, Will Rogers reported an interview with Henry Ford in Dearborn at a time when another car was supposed to be going to cut quite a dash in the Ford sales:

Will Rogers: Mr. Ford, in case those opposition things get to cutting the price and all, just how cheap could you sell your car?

Henry Ford: Well, Will, that is kind of personal but if the worst comes to the worst, I could give it away, as long as we retain the selling of the parts. You know,

Will, one of those things will shake off enough in a year to pay for itself.

The Model T satisfied the typical American's desire to go places and do things. It put him in the driver's seat with his own trusty hands on the wheel, fulfilling his national craving for freedom. During the Depression a hard-times housewife voiced the spirit of the average American in answering a social investigator's query as to why the family went without a bathtub but spent money for a car.

"Well, mister," the housewife replied, "you can't get to town in a bathtub!"

In good truth, the family car was among the important builders of the Bridge, the family car familiar on today's roads and the family car that long since has disappeared from the road, the Stutz Bearcat, the Stanley Steamer, the Pierce Arrow, and so many others that paved the approaches to Highways Over Broad Waters. But of all these, the Merry Olds and the Tin Liz led the way.

When the American in his self-propelled room on wheels came to a water barrier that could be crossed only by ferry boat, he blew his horn in disgust, he sounded his klaxon in anger. He was frustrated. No longer in charge of the situation, he had to wait and depend on transportation other than his own. This robbed him of his sense of power, but crossing a bridge in his car added to his sense of power. Under the surface pride, there lurked a sense of sharing in the great accomplishment of the builders of the bridge. The driver and all his passengers shared in the triumph over nature and her barriers as their car went high above the water gap where the ferry boats no longer were needed.

It was a happy coincidence, and perhaps a kind of

poetic justice, that the dedication year of the Long Crossing, 1958, marked the fiftieth anniversary of the Model T. It took seven years for the one millionth Tin Lizzie or Flivver to roll off the assembly line, but it took only ten months for the one millionth car to cross Mackinac Bridge. However, Henry Ford's all-purpose model had blazed the trail for all the other cars that had honked their horns for new and longer bridges.

Thanks to the Model T's leadership and inspiration, the few thousand cars of David Steinman's boyhood had reached the incredible total of 65 million motor vehicles in the United States, and, to accommodate them, there were 300 thousand highway bridges on three million miles of roads.

Starting with the first Merry Oldsmobile with its curved dashboard and the first Model T with its sober coat of black, the cars of America had joined in a parade leading inevitably to where the Straits of Mackinac kept them from going any further under their own power. They honked their horns impatiently at the crawling ferry boats while they waited for a master bridge-builder to meet the challenge of such a broad water barrier.

But for a long time it seemed as if the cars would never make the long crossing under their own power. The man born and raised to meet the ultimate challenge of the Straits of Mackinac had made a decision as hard and as lonesome as the one made by Henry Ford. On that decision depended success for his profession or a life of bitter failure for himself.

David B. Steinman, born in the shadows of a long-span bridge, brought up in a city where long-span bridges were a-building, whose whole career had been inspired by and dedicated to long-span bridges, might never again build a long-span bridge!

Fourteen

Electric Fan & 50c Cardboard Bridge Model

In yon strait path a thousand
May well be stopped by three.
Now who will stand on either hand
And keep the bridge with me?

Horatius at the Bridge

THE OLD LAKES SAILOR sat forward in his captain's chair and squinted out the roadway of Mackinac Bridge toward where the towers rose and the suspension cables roller-coasted over the Straits. "Imagine a Roman soldier standing out there in the middle," he told the School Reporter, "trying to hold back the enemy so his own people could be saved."

"I can recite almost the whole poem by heart," bragged the School Reporter.

"Well, son, David B. Steinman was a kind of Horatius at the Bridge, and he held the strait path against all opposition for more years than you've been born, but most people thought he was a wrong-headed Don Quixote fighting with windmills."

The gravest hour of Steinman's life struck when he was building the Thousand Islands International Bridge across the St. Lawrence River between the United States and Canada. Two weeks before the scheduled opening celebration, the resident engineer at the bridge site put in a long-distance call to his boss.

110

"I'm worried, sir," he reported. "The bridge is acting up. The suspension span is doing some very peculiar things."

"Give me a technical description," Steinman said, his heart in his throat.

"There are vertical heaving motions of the bridge floor. I've never seen, or even heard about, anything like it in my life."

Steinman took the next train from New York, but when he arrived at the bridge he could observe no motion in the suspension span. "What kind of wind did you have when this happened?"

"A quartering wind," the resident engineer replied.

"I'll wait right here until it comes from that direction again," Steinman decided, hoping against hope that all this could be the other's imagination.

But when the wind came, the bridge started a slow heaving, like a man's chest in breathing. Along with this up-and-down heaving, and in the same rhythm, the suspension span had a gentle back-and-forth longitudinal motion from tower to tower. It was something strange not only to Steinman but unknown in bridge engineering history.

"Perhaps it's one of the mysterious phenomena that were responsible for great bridge disasters of the past," he thought to himself, "tragic wrecks that could have been prevented if someone had looked into the reasons for such failures without going ahead blind and building bridges that were guesswork rather than guaranteed of safety."

He had two decisions to make, the one involving years of study and experiment, but the other had to be made on the spot. There was a deadline to meet, and there were three possible things he could do.

First, he could let the dedication ceremonies go ahead

without trying to do anything about the strange motions of the span. He could trust to luck that there would be no accidents. But he had never trusted to luck and didn't intend to start now.

Second, he could call off the dedication ceremonies until he had a fair chance to solve the mystery and work out a solution. But the invitations had been sent out, all arrangements had been made. A last-minute cancellation would result in unfavorable publicity and might cause serious financial harm to the backers of the bridge.

Third, the only remaining alternative was for the engineer in charge to invent a way out of the trouble, to stop the motions of the span and make it safe.

With no time to lose, and under terrific pressure, the onetime schoolboy nicknamed the Steam Engine because his ideas always ran ahead of his tongue, put on his thinking cap and came up with a two-part answer to the problem. He figured out a pair of inclined stays forming an inverted V at the middle of the suspension span, rigidly connecting the stiffening girder to the cable at that point, and thereby stopping the back-and-forth motion from tower to tower. This also tended to prevent the heaving up-and-down motion which the wind started almost the way a child's swing is pushed, building up higher and higher in momentum until the faltering or twisting stage would be reached. But, to prevent the heaving motion altogether, he decided to use end-span cable stays, two or more inclined wire ropes or rope-strands, running radially from the ends of the span to selected points on the cable.

"Instead of that, sir," the resident engineer butted in at this point, "I'd very respectfully suggest inclined rope-stays *beneath* the roadway, anchoring the span to the piers, similar to the guy-ropes the builder of the Brooklyn Bridge used to anchor his Niagara Railway

Suspension Bridge to the rock-walls of the Niagara Gorge, to prevent wind uplift of the span."

His mind a million light-years or so ahead of this member of his staff, Steinman nodded in polite agreement. "Your idea might work, but any such hold-down stays on our span here would be an obstruction and hazard to navigation. Besides, we can get exactly the same effect by moving the location of the inclined guy-ropes *upward,* from the seemingly obvious position *underneath* the span to a less obvious but more scientific position *above* the span, between the span and the cables."

The resident engineer looked puzzled. It was hard for him to understand such a novel and basic idea. He shook his head and shrugged: "These Eggheads!"

With the bridgemen on the job working at top speed around the clock, they installed Steinman's emergency repairs on time, making the suspension span stable and safe. The rope-stays were so inconspicuous that the twenty thousand people who thronged the scene on the day of the bridge dedication never noticed them. They had no shadow of realization that, only by the narrowest margin, had the gala festivities been made possible.

After the hoop-la and hurrahs had come to an end, David B. Steinman took a long and final look at the Thousand Islands International Bridge. He had reached the hard and lonesome decision that was to become an historic landmark in bridge engineering. "I've built my last long-span bridge," he announced quietly, "until I find out how to make them absolutely safe."

"But, sir," the resident engineer protested, "this bridge *is* safe."

"Now it is," Steinman agreed, "but it wasn't before, and I don't intend to build another long-span bridge until I've found out the secret of perfect aerodynamic stability, until I can build a bridge that will stand up against the force of any wind coming from any direction. My next long-span will be able to take winds of up to 600 miles an hour, up to 900 miles an hour, up to infinity!"

"But, sir," the resident engineer said in the soothing way a nurse addresses a very sick person, "that's not reasonable, sir, that's impossible."

"Here in America," said the Manhattan Islander born of immigrant parents, "we've got a very old and a very true saying: 'The impossible just takes a little more time.' "

It took David B. Steinman seventeen years. They were years of loneliness and heartache because he had to go his own way regardless of professional opposition and against friendly advice, but they were years that blazed a trail in the annals of bridge engineering as surely as the voyageurs blazed the Northwest Passage.

When Steinman had observed the uneasy motion of his Thousand Islands Bridge, he had been carried back to that unforgettable moment during college days when the great Professor Burr had walked soberly into the engineering classroom with a grim telegram in his fingers. His words echoed across the years:

"Gentlemen, I have just received the tragic news that the Quebec Bridge, the world's largest, has collapsed while under construction."

David Steinman did not want his dreams haunted by the possibility that he might awake one morning to be told that a bridge of his had fallen during the night. As he bent every effort toward discovering the secret of perfect safety, he warned other builders of long spans that they were taking too much risk with too little knowledge of the mysterious forces which had wrecked large bridges of the past.

But Steinman's rivals scoffed at him, and some of them laughed openly when they saw the nature of his experiments and the poverty of his equipment. Unable to afford expensive wind-tunnel tests, he had reverted back to schoolboy days when he had invented a combination cradle and rocker for tired mothers, operated a Dutch windmill with an electric fan, and tested cardboard bridge models by spanning the aisle between armchair desks in the classroom. Now he used the breeze from an office fan to test a fifty-cent cardboard model of a bridge.

A reporter, peeking over the transom door after he had been boosted up on the shoulders of a companion, let out a silent whistle and motioned to be let down. "Let's get out of here," he whispered, shaking his head gravely. "I don't know what's happened to poor Steinman. Instead of performing this world-shaking experiment I figured would make a great news story, he's sitting in there with his feet on the desk watching a toy bridge that he blows around with an office fan."

Competitors in the engineering field were less kind than the reporter when they found out what Steinman was doing. "He's gone completely off his rocker," they said. "The Egghead's lost all his buttons."

Steinman had delivered his warning. He paid no further attention to rivals. Bridges were his lifework. He believed he had been placed on earth to serve a special purpose: to build *Highways Over Broad Waters.*
From earliest boyhood he had looked upon bridges, not as mere shapes of cold stone and metal, but as creations that could come alive and warm and beautiful. He recognized the importance of bridges. The progress of a nation could be measured by the bridges built. The history of any war could be told in the bridges destroyed.

He saw that every bridge stood as a symbol of many things: an extension, a leap over, a thrust forward, a gangway, a plank from the past across the present into the future, an adult realization of boyhood's buildings in the sand, a sign of hope, an act of faith, a symbol of man's yearning to be free, a civilized rainbow arched through time, a magic carpet, a flying horse, a fairy wand, a monument to man's eternal quest of the beauty that is truth and the truth that is beauty in art, in science, and in all pursuits of life.

As a seven-year-old newsboy selling papers under the massive shadows of the Brooklyn Bridge, David B. Steinman had dedicated his life to bridges. Now he did not begrudge lonesome years spent in searching out the secret ways that would make them safe. Slowly, day by day and month after month, as he allowed the electric fan to play upon various cardboard models that he built, some of the secrets were revealed to him. He found that bridge sections of a certain shape would gallop or dance in the breeze of the fan while others would let the wind slip through their open spaces like water flowing through a sieve.

Just as he was beginning to feel sure of victory, a thunderclap of doom struck one of the bridges he had warned the builders against. Out West in the state of Washington, a forty-mile gale whipped across the Tacoma Narrows and the suspension span located there went into a dance of death. The storm-tossed waters of Puget Sound swallowed the twisted wreckage as it came plunging down.

"Fortunately no human lives were lost," a report said. "A newspaper reporter was the last man on the bridge. He had to abandon his car and make his way off the heaving span by crawling on his hands and knees and desperately clutching the curb. His dog, refusing to leave the car, stood guard to the last and went down with the ruins."

Steinman glared at the report. "If they had listened to me," he said in fierce resentment, "the bridge could have been saved — and no dog would have been lost."

People in the profession began to remember Steinman's warnings, voiced so far in the past. They showed a different attitude toward his determination not to build another long-span bridge until he had solved the problem of perfect aerodynamic stability. They looked with new respect upon his office fan and the fifty-cent cardboard model.

He had reached the end of the lonesome road. The secrets of perfect bridge safety were in his grasp. He knew that at last he could build a suspension span as airy and delicate as a fine lace pattern, as beautiful as frozen music, and yet as strong and enduring as steel. The wind, any wind from any direction, would slide away, slip through, never harm the structure.

Word got around that Steinman's experiments with a toy bridge and an electric fan had solved more suspension span problems than all the wind tunnel tests ever conducted. Finally, in the mail one morning, came a letter postmarked Mackinac Island. It was from W. Stewart Woodfill, President of the fabulous Grand Hotel. In effect, the letter said:

"I'm Chairman of the Mackinac Bridge Citizens Committee. We'd like your expert advice. Do you think it possible to build a bridge across the Straits?"

Steinman smiled across his desk at an electric fan and a fifty-cent cardboard model that were a little the worse for wear. Then he picked up his pen and wrote:

"Yes, Mr. Woodfill, I now can give you every assurance that a bridge across the Straits of Mackinac is entirely possible. We can make the Long Crossing . . . ."

Fifteen

Hail the Conquering Heroes

Hail to the victors valiant,
Hail to the conquering heroes,
Hail hail to Michigan
The champions of the West!

WITH HIS MOUTH open and his eyes wide, the School Reporter listened as the old Lakes sailor hopped off his captain's chair all of a sudden to wave his Irish pipe like a baton and bellow out the Michigan Victor's Song.

"Did you go to Michigan, sir?"

"Nope, son, I started out on the Lakes as a cook's helper when I was twelve, but that's never stopped me from cheering, come every football Saturday." The Watchman's eyes crinkled at their weatherbeaten corners. "But what I really stood up to cheer about this time was the conquering heroes who built this bridge and gave Michigan two champions of the West and of the world, the Soo Canal and Mackinac Bridge!"

When David B. Steinman came to the Straits of Mackinac, hired to build a bridge that many people considered impossible, he recognized himself as one in a long line of builders stretching back to the dawn of history, to the misty days when salt-water seas had rolled across the Upper Great Lakes region, when countless trillions and septillions of animals and fish had left their shells and bones behind so that there might be limestone to smelt the iron ore of the Killarney Moun-

tains into the bridge towers and the rollercoasting suspension cables and the long spans in between. From
the Killarney Mountains, too, had come the copper to
supply the wires and conduits for the bridge, and give
the span its fairytale necklace of pearls each night.

All this David Steinman realized. He regarded every
bridge as the work of many, as a highway of destiny,
representing not merely the success of one man but
progress for the millions. And he looked upon a bridge
not only as a triumph for the builders but also as a
form of creative art in which all who made the passage
across shared in the act of creation again. Every time
a car crossed a bridge, he felt, the driver and passengers
participated actively in the triumph over nature that
the original builders had achieved.

In Steinman's mind and heart, it was this quality of
sharing that gave bridges the mystery and magic they
had held for people across the ages.

Looking out across the restless broad waters of the
Straits, Steinman could see from afar the line high up
on Mackinac Island that traced the old beachhead of
glacier-born Lake Algonquin. In the distance he saw
the various islands that, according to the legends of the
Ottawas and the Ojibways, were the wreckage of the
bridge once built by Hiawatha.

In his imagination Steinman could see the ghost
canoes and phantom sails of yesterday, beating around
the Straits in search of the fabled Northwest Passage,
beating back with their cargoes of furs, blazing trails
toward tomorrow. He saw the traffic of today at the
Crossroads of the Great Lakes, the long ore and grain
carriers, the cement boats, the iron-jawed ferries crowded
with impatient automobiles. All these, the ancient
voyageur and the modern vacationer, the old-fashioned
and the new-fangled methods of transportation, he

recognized as builders of the bridge entrusted to him
now for its final shape and form.

Thinking these thoughts, and feeling his grave respon-
sibility, he stared in awe at the vast expanse of water
to be bridged. One shore was hardly visible from the
other. His awe changed to a silent prayer.

Before turning away, he took in a sweeping view of
the Straits, including one of the ferry boats that was
plowing across carrying cars that had lost their power
for an hour. Instead of long waits in line and then a
long tiresome haul, he made up his mind to give them a
thrilling ten-minute ride under their own power, with
no waits in any weather and skyscraper views along the
way.

In his office he bent over his drafting board with the
realization that the last engineer who had planned a
bridge across the Straits would have seen his work
wrecked by the wind before it could be completed. As
Steinman drew his designs and pored over blueprints,
he carried on a conversation with an imaginary someone
named Nosiree.

Nosiree (shaking his head hopelessly) : Steinman,
get some sense into your head. You'd be better off
to give up before you start. It's no use. You'll never
be able to sink foundations down through that water
and into the bottom of that glacial gorge. There's
nothing but a honeycomb of prehistoric caverns below
and it'll collapse under the weight of your piers.

Steinman (beaming) : I've got news for you, Nosiree.
I hired geologists to make test borings, and those caverns
you're grumbling about collapsed into solid rock many
thousand years ago, rock so solid that it could support
four times the weight of the bridge.

Nosiree (scowling): But what about the ice? Wait'll
the winter sends it slamming into your bridge piers.

Wait'll those juggernauts of ice grind down from Lake Superior and around from Lake Huron and up from Lake Michigan to meet in the middle of the Straits of Mackinac and wipe your bridge off the map.

Steinman (jotting down figures to show Nosiree): I've tested the pressure of winter ice at its worst and I've tested the pressure of ice under laboratory conditions, and I'm designing a bridge that will be twenty times as strong as any ice pressure that can possibly be brought against it. Just for good measure, I'll put armor plate on the piers. I don't care if another glacier comes down from Hudson Bay. The bridge won't budge.

Nosiree (triumphantly): How about the wind? No bridge ever built could stand the wind at the Straits of Mackinac. Have you forgotten that the Tacoma Narrows Bridge buckled and fell to pieces in a forty-mile-an-hour gale? Up at the Straits that's nothing more than a fresh breeze. Seventy miles an hour is just cruising speed for a Mackinac wind.

Steinman (nodding in agreement): You're right about the force of the wind at the Straits. I've clocked it at almost eighty miles an hour myself. But have you forgotten my experiments with the electric fan and that fifty-cent cardboard model? Those experiments showed me a way to build a bridge that can stand any velocity of wind at any angle of attack.

Nosiree (skeptically): You can build a bridge on paper, but let's see what happens on the job! You'll never make it. Nosiree!

But ground was broken and bridgemen went to work according to Steinman's plans, May 8, 1954, an historic date in bridgebuilding history. On November 1, 1957, the last car-ferry trip was made across the Straits and the Mackinac Bridge welcomed the world on wheels.

Between these dates, some three and a half years apart, Steinman issued orders that sent deep-water divers out to blast the pier foundations down to bedrock, more than two hundred feet below the level of the Straits. He gave encouragement to the caisson and cofferdam crews who took off across treacherous seas to set the forms for the towers and piers and pour the concrete from their wave-tossed floating equipment. He rode the tugs that shouldered huge steel spans into position so they could be hoisted and derricked up to the main structure. He stepped to the top of the twin towers before they were completed, and he walked the spider threads of the parallel catwalks as they made their loop-the-loop to blaze a trail for the suspension cables to follow.

He watched three Michigan winters do their worst in threatening to destroy the bridge before the Long Crossing had reached full strength. He saw car-ferries trapped in ice that even the Coast Guard Icebreaker *Mackinaw* had trouble rescuing them from. He stood calm while moving mountains of ice with crests thirty feet high crashed into bridge piers. He held his breath at the spring breakup spectacle of icebergs bellowing through the Straits like a herd of rogue elephants.

But, as he had promised Nosiree, the bridge did not budge.

Nor did Mackinac Bridge show any signs of strain when a wind almost twice as strong as the one that had wrecked the Tacoma Narrows Bridge came blasting a-cross the Straits during the second November of the job. Despite the fact that they still lacked about half of the 220 thousand rivets necessary to each of them for maximum reinforcement, the two towers out in mid-stream withstood the icy siege of a 76-mile-an-hour hurricane.

The steel lacework of the bridge let the wind slip

through.   The Mackinac had been built to *ride* the gales and hurricanes of the Upper Great Lakes.   Like some of the cars that had played their part in building him, he was *streamlined*, he had *floating power*, he belonged to the *jet age*.

There were 85 thousand blueprints used in building the Mackinac Bridge.   A million tons of concrete and steel and 20 million manhours of sweat and toil and courage and sacrifice went into its construction.   Five men gave their lives to help build the bridge.

A number of veteran bridgemen could not take the awesome combination of dizzy heights and troubled water.   After pleading illness a few times when huge sections of steelwork were to be towed out into the Straits and hung against the skyline, they packed their kits and left Mackinac.   The *gandy dancers* and *hard-hats* who stayed to the finish carried themselves with the swaggering pride of voyageurs as they left for the far corners of the earth to take a hand in building dams, tunnels, railroads, atomic plants, and other bridges.

One of the young bridgemen looked back a minute at the great road across the water, and then spoke for all his fellow workers: "None of us'll ever forget Long Mack.   He's the *most*.   When I'm an old man all crippled up with rheumatism and wearing a long white beard, I'll tell my grandchildren how I helped build Mackinac Bridge!"

Just as the Soo Canal could be called a monument to Charles T. Harvey and his canal gangs of a century ago, so could the Long Crossing be called a monument to David B. Steinman and all the builders of the bridge — a monument as enduring as the pyramids.

One day, during the course of construction, a boss on the job had come up to Steinman and said:

"Doctor, I believe you've made an important mistake in a decimal point."

The bridge-builder, startled by the remark and wondering what might have gone wrong, asked: "What do you mean?"

"Well, Doctor, you've been telling people that this bridge is good for a century. But I want to go on record right now as saying that Mackinac Bridge will be standing a thousand years from now!"

Sixteen

Navigating the Straits in a Model T

I lift my span, I fling it wide,
I stand where wind and wave contend.
I bear the load so men may ride
Whither they will, and to what end.
                    Steinman's Song of the Bridge.

"ALL RIGHT, SON," the Watchman told the School Reporter, leading the way off the bridge approach. "Let's go for that ride."

Taking his young friend in tow, the old Lakes captain with the gold anchor design on his blue skipper cap charted a course down to the parking area in Mackinaw City where the antique touring car with the shamrock doors and the brass schooner whistle stood waiting to take them across Mackinac Bridge.

"Don't mind fresh air, do you?" the Watchman grinned. "The old girl's got a top that can be put up in case of rain and such, but if we hoisted canvas now a gust of wind might pick us up out in the middle of the bridge and carry us like a weather balloon over to Wisconsin or up to Canada. Hop in, son!"

First the young man in the school jacket walked all around the car, staring at the high wheels with the wooden spokes and the queer looking tires that seemed only a little bit larger than those on his sister's bicycle. He stood on the running board that was a sort of stairstep to the front and back seats. Next to the modern cars in the parking area, it struck him that the ungainly Model T was like an extinct animal in a museum, with nothing but bones showing.

"Does it really work?" he asked doubtfully.

"Like I told you, son, even Henry Ford was kind of surprised when the first one showed signs of life. But this here and now Flivver is the car that put the world on wheels and paved the way for bigger and better bridges, including Long Mack."

Shaking his head and making shorthand notes of his own invention, the School Reporter retraced his steps to the back end of the Model T and looked high and low for something. Finally, after getting down and peering under the axle, he made a puzzled inquiry:

"Where's the gas tank?"

"Under the front seat, naturally, where a gas tank ought to be," the Watchman chuckled, lifting back the seat and showing the oval tank underneath. Then he unscrewed a metal cap and poked a handy measuring stick down the hole. It came up with the bottom inch wet.

"Should be plenty to get us across," the grizzled sailor estimated. "If we run out while we're on the span, I've got an emergency bottle of raspberry shrub we can always pour in. A Tin Lizzie will run on anything."

Obeying instructions the School Reporter climbed into the driver's seat while the Watchman took hold of the crank attached to the front of the flivver. He had made the social error of asking where the starter was located, and the other had answered irritably:

"Son, the self starter, that's me!"

The boy gazed in bewilderment at the two levers attached on each side of the steering wheel and at the three pedals on the floorboard where modern cars had one or at most two pedals for clutch and brake.

"The left pedal's the biggest part of your gear shift," the Watchman explained patiently. "Push it down a little ways and that's first, push it clear to the floorboard and that's second, let it kick back and you're in high. The middle pedal is reverse, and the right pedal is the brake."

"Boy, it must have been hard to learn to drive in the old days, with all these levers and pedals and things!"

"All the modern push-button gadgets haven't solved the hardest problem," the Watchman said seriously. "Nobody's figured out a way to cut down accidents by regulating the nut that's attached to the steering wheel!"

"The nut attached to the steering wheel? Oh, I see!"

The old sailor gave the crank a practice turn or two and then, still bent over, he poked a deep-water blue eye over the radiator top at the boy sitting enthroned behind the high uncompromisingly straight double-decked windshield.

"Keep your foot down tight on the brake, son, while I'm cranking," he warned, "because these things champ at the bit like a horse feeling his oats and they've run down more than one owner that wasn't spry on his feet. They got too much get-up-and-go to stay in neutral. Another thing you have to be careful about is those levers on the steering wheel. The right-hand lever is the throttle, so keep that where she be, about halfway down."

The deep-water blue eye showed an ominous glint above the brass radiator. "And mind what I told you about the left-hand lever. That's the spark, and if you don't keep it all the way up while I'm cranking, this handle's liable to kick back and spin around on me and break my wrist. But as quick as I get the old girl perking, pull the spark lever down most of the way."

"Yes, sir," said the School Reporter, deeply aware

Dick Rienstra

of his responsibilities. "Shall I turn on the ignition key?" At a nod he did so, and a box of coils under the dashboard began to buzz like an angry rattlesnake.

The Watchman bent over the crank and gave it half a spin. The motor coughed and died. "Needs a little stronger feed," decided the old Lakes sailor, pulling with his left hand at a wire attached to what he called "the choke," and spinning the crank with his right.

The Model T came to life with a roar, starting to lunge forward, but the School Reporter clamped hard on the brake and pulled down the spark lever. The engine sound smoothed out and the boy slid over on the front seat as the Watchman hopped on the running board, hoisted himself into the driver's place by hooking his leg over the door panel, and gave fair warning that they were about to set sail by pumping the schooner whistle and pushing down the handle of the Klaxon horn.

Everyone within sight and sound turned to gawk as the old Lakes sailor drove his foot to the floorboard on the left pedal and the Model T shot forward, as the driver commented to his passenger, "Like a Porcupine Mountain jackrabbit with forty-nine dollars worth of firecrackers tied to his tail!"

The top of his head seven feet off the pavement of the bridge approach, the School Reporter could look down from what seemed a great height on the lowslung modern cars. "Hold on to your seat, hold on to your hat, just plain hold on!" the Watchman had advised as they took off, and the boy was following the advice for dear life as they began to navigate the Straits of Mackinac on wheels.

"H-h-how f-fast are we g-g-going, s-sir?"

"H-h-how should I know, s-son?" the Watchman replied, making an iron effort to keep his own teeth from chattering with every bounce and rattle of old Tin Liz. "They d-didn't m-m-make any f-fancy doo-dads like speedometers f-for these things!"

As the two Model T voyageurs grew accustomed to the motion while the car rode high over the Crossroads of the Great Lakes, soaring above the ghosts of Pere Marquette's canot du maitre and LaSalle's ill-fated Griffin as well as the latest long ship passing from the iron mines to the steel mills, the Watchman, sometimes leaving only one hand on the precarious wheel in order to point with the other, acted the role of a tourist guide.

"Long Mack's got thirty-four piers, son, and all but two of them are in water. His muscles were built up from one million tons of concrete and steel. He can carry as many cars in one week as the whole car-ferry fleet used to haul across the Straits in a year. Young Mister Big's canal gangs up at Sault Ste. Marie used to say they was digging a ditch that ran a mile and a little bit more. The Long Crossing's got a stretch of *five* miles and a little bit more."

Down below one of the long ships blew for passage, the hoots reaching the bridge thin with distance. In answering salute, the weathered Lake captain pumped his old schooner whistle from the Model T while passing motorists almost fell out their windows in curiosity.

A young couple in a new convertible kept pace along-side for a minute or so, and finally the girl called across: "Are you part of some parade?"

"You bet!" the Watchman yelled back. "A parade that started in Detroit fifty years ago and kept going to beat the band until it drummed up enough business to build this bridge!"

Up ahead the towers of the suspension span began to loom larger against the sky as the Model T drove forward with all four cylinders racing. Looking out over the bridge rail across the wide waters at huge ore carriers dwarfed by the height from which they were observed, the School Reporter felt like Gulliver in the land of the Lilliputians. "How high are we, sir?"

"Well, son, the Seven Wonders of the Ancient World have got nothing on us. We just passed over the Colossus of Rhodes, and our wheels never even touched. The Mackinac Bridge's towers stand almost twice as tall above water as the Tower of Babel and the Hanging Gardens of Babylon, and each of them can top the Great Pyramid by a good fifty-two feet. They could bow to the waist and kiss the Statue of Liberty on the forehead, and they can look the Washington Monument and Detroit's tallest skyscraper smack in the eye."

The School Reporter was trying to take notes, but the shaking of the flivver made it difficult. Besides the radiator caught his attention and held him fascinated. Bubbles of water were being forced out through the brass cap that he had seen the Watchman twist tight, and steam was rising like an Indian smoke signal. "Sir," he began.

"Don't bother your head about it, son," the old Lakes sailor reassured the boy. "Lizzie here gets excited every time she makes the Long Crossing. You can't blame her for getting overheated when she navigates the greatest bridge in creation. Keep an eye peeled and, if she threatens to blow her top, we'll trot out some emergency medicine."

Sounding more like a steam engine every minute, the Model T continued her indomitable course across the Straits of Mackinac. She was approaching South Anchorage, one of the two massive concrete piers that marked each end of the suspension bridge located at midstream.

"You see, old son," the Watchman explained, "Long Mack goes marching out across more water than most bridges ever see before he even begins to commence to become a suspension bridge. We've already put sixteen regular bridge piers and sections behind us, we're a country mile from shore and ten office stories high, and we're just arriving at the place where the south ends of the suspension cables are anchored down. Want some figures to jot down?"

"Yes, sir," the School Reporter said, one eye on his notepad and the other held spellbound by the steaming radiator.

"Well, there's enough pencil-sized wire in those cables to go almost twice around the world or a sixth of the way to the moon. All that wire, no thicker than your little finger, had to be strung from each anchorage across the Straits and high over the towers until both of the cables were as big around as a barrel."

The veteran Lakes sailor paused his conversation to blow the Model T's schooner whistle at a green-hulled fishtug passing far below. "We're rolling over Pier 17 now, South Anchorage, the beginning of the suspension part of Mackinac Bridge. This anchorage, same as the one at the other end of the span, was built of about 85 thousand cubic yards of concrete and can resist a total pull from both cables of around sixty million pounds. Those are vital statistics, son, because it's the cables that hold up the roadway we're starting out on, and we'll be depending on those cables until we get to Pier 22, South Anchorage, which is more than a mile and a half away."

The steaming radiator was forgotten as the thrilling ride over a suspension bridge longer than the famed Golden Gate structure in San Francisco brought the heart of the Long Crossing's story to the School Reporter's full realization. He followed with widening eyes the soar and the sag of the cables, and he gasped at the height of each sentinel tower as the Model T passed between the massive portals. Although he had memorized figures and jotted down statistics, he now understood for the first time, as he made the crossing himself, that out here at mid-Straits, counting only six of his thirty-four piers the Mackinac was greater than any other bridge in world history.

But at last the overwrought state of Tin Lizzie's emotions could not be ignored. The front of the car was enveloped in steam, and the Watchman had to pull over to the side of the bridge just after they drove across North Anchorage and onto the regular roadway of the Bridge. Whipping out a bandana to protect his hands, he untwisted the radiator cap and then rummaged around under the back seat of the car until he located a quart bottle of pink liquid.

"Emergency medicine," he chortled, pouring the contents into the radiator. "Helped put life into the builders of the Soo Canal and Mackinac Bridge both. Raspberry shrub. Good for man or beast or Model T."

With its radiator quieted down below the boiling point, the flivver drove up in style to the toll gate on the St. Ignace side of the Long Crossing where the old Lakes sailor paid the fare. A large whitehaired man standing nearby nodded pleasantly and said, "Have a cigar, Captain?"

"Thanks, Senator." The Watchman took the offering and stuffed it into his pipe, chuckling. "I was beginning to worry I might have to buy one myself!"

"Who's the senator?" the School Reporter asked as they drove away.

"That's Prentiss M. Brown, head of the Mackinac Bridge Authority. Lots of people in Michigan call him *Mister Bridge*." The Watchman waved his hand in the direction of Mackinac Island. "He used to be a bellhop at a hotel over there, working for ten-cent tips. How's that for a start toward bossing a hundred million dollar bridge, son?"

A newsboy waved a paper at the Model T, and the Watchman jammed on the brake to get a second look at the headline:

DR. STEINMAN VISITS LONG MACK
INSPECTS BRIDGE SITE AT SOO

The School Reporter turned to the old Lakes sailor, a question glowing in his eager eyes.

"Okay, son," the Watchman said, "let's go and find him. The Mackinac Bridge story for your school paper won't be complete unless you get a personal interview with the number one bridge-builder of all time."

Seventeen

Long Mack's Happy Birthday

So day after day
He stitched and tinkered and hammered away,
Till at last 't was done, —
The greatest invention under the sun!

Darius Green

THE WATCHMAN and the School Reporter rode all over the town of St. Ignace in search of Dr. Steinman, leaving word at the barber shop, the weekly newspaper office, the public library, and the Mackinac Bridge Authority headquarters that they were looking for him.

"I couldn't even begin to tell you where to find him," Larry Rubin, executive secretary of the Authority, said with a hopeless shrug. "We'd like to do lots of things in honor of his visit, but there's the chauffeur and the private limousine we got for him, standing idle at the curb, and he's simply disappeared into thin air."

The Model T seemed to strain forward in the hunt, snuffling as if she were a bloodhound on the leash. It turned out that the snuffling sound was caused by escaping steam, and then she developed an alarming knock.

The Watchman cocked his head forward and listened, his face grave as a heart specialist who knew all his patients' symptoms. "That's a bad knock in Number One Cylinder," he said, pulling over onto the shoulder of the road and switching off the ignition key. With an air of a doctor deciding on exactly the right prescription,

he rummaged around under the back seat cushion until
he brought out an apothecary jar full of white balls the
size of shooting agates.

Wrinkling his nose, the School Reporter said: "They
smell like moth balls."

"Yup." The old Lakes sailor unscrewed the brass
cap and thoughtfully dropped three of the moth balls
into the radiator. "They look to be about the right size
pills for this big car, and they sniff bad enough to be
good for what ails anybody."

The School Reporter had to scramble to his feet as
the Watchman lifted up the front seat cushion to take
off the top of the gas tank and inject a milder dose of
two moth balls. "But, sir, do those things really help?"

"Well, son, the treatment don't hurt *her,* and it helps
me; makes me feel I've done something for her." The
Watchman affectionately patted the Model T's fender
the way a farmer might pat a faithful horse. "Now we'll
just let her cool off and rest a spell. These flivvers have
got such strong constitutions that, given a little kindness
and a few minutes to stand idle, they'll cure themselves.
While we're waiting, I'll tell you about Long Mack's
Happy Birthday."

What the Watchman called Long Mack's Birthday was
the Bridge Dedication Festival celebrated during the
last week of June, 1958, when the Straits area featured
historical pageants, fireworks, speeches by top-hatted dig-
nitaries, the traditional walk across the span led by
Governor Williams with a sunflower seed in his mouth
to give him strength for the five-mile hike, the parade
of beauty queens and celebrities in dazzling white con-
vertibles riding high over the Cross-roads of the Great
Lakes, and everything else under the sun that a celebration should have.

Watchman (drily) : Trouble was, the sun didn't show

up the first couple of days and it began to look like he might never come to the party at all!

With half a million people expected to be on deck for the climax of the ceremonies on the weekend, the weatherman came out with ominous news. Twisters hit Kansas and Indiana, and funnel clouds were reported over southern Michigan in the wake of severe thunderstorms. These reports of tornado winds cast a black shadow on Long Mack's happy birthday celebration.

Meanwhile, as the historical pageants recreated the days when arrows and tomahawks were guided missiles and the only landing craft were birchbark canoes, the Mackinac Bridge Authority's Chairman, Prentiss M. Brown, announced that, to help celebrate Long Mack's birthday:

"The military will do just about everything but launch a satellite from the center of the bridge."

In fact, Army Secretary Brucker even ordered an Explorer satellite sent up from the Redstone arsenal at Huntsville, Alabama, and it was so small (80 inches long) compared with the bridge and all the big missiles on display that everyone lost track of it until a reporter spotted the space vehicle propped up against a hot water pipe in the basement of the Mackinac Bridge Authority's office. Finally a place was found to put on public display the future inhabitant of outer space, the Explorer of stars that would one day keep an electronic eye on Long Mack as the satellite went into orbit. At the northern end of the bridge, those who came to see the trailblazing span also could observe the tiny trailblazer of interstellar space.

True to the announcement made by "Mr. Bridge," a full-scale war could have been waged with the missiles, planes, tanks, ships, and "top brass" that invaded northern Michigan to help dedicate the Long Crossing. The armed forces at hand and on deck were larger, and far more powerful, than could be found in many countries.

On Wednesday, June 25, the rain came down in torrents as the Mackinac Bridge commemorative stamp and first-day covers went on sale, but no amount of downpour could have darkened the day for David B. Steinman. He was an avid stamp collector along with his own two sons, and the drawing he had made in designing the bridge had been chosen for the design of the stamp. To add to this thrill of a lifetime, Postmaster General Summerfield during a luncheon at the Grand Hotel on Mackinac Island, presented Steinman with a special album containing one of the first sheets of the new commemorative stamp, autographed by Uncle Sam's number one mailman.

The weather worsened overnight and, during the small hours on Thursday, the North Country, as if to test the new bridge in full view of the scores of thousands assembled in the Straits area, put on a show all its own, a real blow-out, with a steady breeze clocked by the Coast Guard on Mackinac Island at seventy miles an hour. Gusts of eighty-two miles an hour were reported near the bridge at St. Ignace.

While driving rain and high winds raked the northland, Dr. Steinman, staying at a Lodge near St. Ignace, went to bed and slept soundly with never a bad dream about the bridge. But military officials reported extensive damage to their displays on both sides of the span. Trees, tents, signs, banners, TV antennas, and even steel buildings were toppled by the storms. Power lines went crashing down. Festival floats were blown end over end and ruined. Events had to be cancelled as multitudes took any available shelter. Governor Williams, due to attend commemorative ceremonies on the mainland, had to remain stranded on Mackinac Island when all ferry service was halted because of turbulent air and choppy seas. A large yacht went aground near the Island's breakwater.

In the wake of the hurricane blasts, Dr. Steinman awoke refreshed from an uninterrupted night's sleep and listened to the news reports while having a hearty breakfast. Then he went outside to the resplendent white convertible that had been assigned to him along with a young soldier in uniform to serve as his chauffeur in the parades and other festivities. He knew from previous talks with his driver that the young man had no knowledge of his real identity as the designer and engineer of the bridge, so he decided to have a little fun.

As the convertible shot forward in the driveway to pick him up and the young soldier saluted as he opened the door, the bridge-builder put on his best poker face and remarked:

"They tell me we had an eighty-two mile wind last night. I wonder whether the bridge is still standing."

"Oh, yes, sir," the young driver said seriously. "That bridge can stand a much stronger wind."

"It can?" Pleased by this youthful reassurance and sign of public faith, Dr. Steinman tried to keep even a twinkle from his eye. "I'm glad to hear you say so," he said gravely. "I really am!"

The weather cleared for the climax of Long Mack's birthday party on Saturday. While beauty queens, coming from each end of the bridge, carried two huge lengths of green ribbon to the center of the span where it was knotted in the middle to form a five-mile bow representing the joining together of Michigan's upper and lower peninsulas, bands played, crowds cheered, cars blew their horns on the bridge and from the shore,

boats whistled and hooted below on the shining Straits
of Mackinac, and overhead flying boxcars and super-
sonic jets made the dream of Darius Green and his Flying Machine come true:

> *I'll astonish the nation,*
> *An' all creation,*
> *By flyin' over the celebration!*

But the highwater mark of Long Mack's Happy
Birthday, as far as Dr. Steinman was concerned, had
come on Friday evening when he opened a letter addressed to him from a youngster in Kalamazoo. It was
written in pencil, in a boyish scrawl.

"Dear Dr. Steinman," he wrote. "My name is David
Steinman too. I am eight years old, and I am in the
third grade. We just got back from a trip to St. Ignace
and saw your big bridge. It is beautiful and big. When
I grow up I want to build a bridge like yours."

Mindful of the dreams of his own boyhood, David B.
Steinman, in the hectic midst of festive doings, dropped
everything to send off a quick reply to his young name-
sake:

"Dear David," he wrote. "I was delighted to hear
from you. It is good to know that you have the same
name as mine. When I was your age I was inspired by
the Brooklyn Bridge and I hoped some day to build a
bridge like the Mackinac Bridge. I hope that your
dream will also come true and that in your time you
will build a bridge even bigger than the Mackinac
Bridge."

During the week-long celebration the Watchman was
very much on deck to see the sights and add his leather-
lunged cheers to those of the crowd. On Saturday, at the
height of proceedings, Prentiss M. Brown heard him
yell:

"Happy Birthday, Long Mack!   And many happy returns!   According to what the construction boss told Dr. Steinman, you've got nine hundred and ninety-nine more Happy Birthdays to go!"

Eighteen

Paul Bunyan's Bridge

Like Babe and Paul,
You might grow tall
Enough to fit a song.
The way to tell a hero is —
He grows the more he's gone!
Paul Bunyan & Babe

WHEN THE MODEL T had cooled down, the Watchman gave the crank another spin while the School Reporter handled the spark, and away went the old car, apparently as good as new, touring St. Ignace on the lookout for Dr. Steinman. But, after rattling around town another hour and exhausting every clue, the motorists gave up the hunt.

They were returning toward the bridge when, rounding a bend in the road along the Straits, the right front tire gave a long sigh and went flat. The Watchman brought the car to a flopping halt, got out and inspected the damage.

"I'll help," the School Reporter volunteered. "We can fix it easy. Where's the spare tire?"

The old lake sailor glared at the youthful optimist. "You'll help, will you? We can fix it easy, can we?" He rolled up his sleeves and spit on his hands. "Listen, son, this isn't your late-model family car and there's no sense having a spare tire when the rims aren't demountable. The rims on a Model T don't come off the

wheel. The tire has to be yanked off the rim and then, after the puncture in the tube is repaired, the tire has to be coaxed back on the rim that's on the wheel. All it takes to do the job is a combination brain surgeon, acrobat, and professional magician. Now stand back and give me room!"

The School Reporter's eyes began to bulge at the equipment the Watchman hauled out from under the back seat cushion: a car jack stamped Little Giant, various sized tire irons and wooden mallets, something that looked like the top of a nutmeg grater, a can labeled Jiffy Patch, and another can labeled Bear-Grip Glue.

"But can't I do something, sir?" the boy begged, after the Watchman had jacked up the front axle and then carried the struggle to close quarters, with his feet braced against the bottom of the tire and both hands yanking at the top.

"Yes, you can, son. Get out of here! This is a private fight. See that pine tree sticking up from that sand dune along the shore? Go over there and sit down with your back to us and let me battle this out to a finish!"

The School Reporter jumped at the note of authority the onetime Great Lakes captain put into his voice. Without a thought of disobeying, he walked up the sand dune, but he found someone else already sitting with his back against the pine tree, a frail-looking little man with thin grey hair. He wore glasses and he had an open book in his lap but he was staring out across the water at the mighty silhouette of the bridge.

The man nodded a pleasant greeting to the boy. "This is a good place to watch Long Mack," he said companionably. "You know, the bridge fits. The North Country's a region of big sky, tall timber, Great Lakes, and now Long Mack!"

"Yes, sir," the School Reporter said, and then a sudden realization made him tinge from head to toe. "I mean, yes, Dr. Steinman."

"How did you recognize me?"

"I don't know. You don't look anything like what I used to imagine a bridgebuilder would look like, but the minute I saw you I *knew*."

"I'll take that as a compliment." Dr. Steinman smiled and held out his hand as he stood up. "I'm very glad to meet you."

The School Reporter introduced himself and shook the outstretched hand with ceremony. He felt like the boy who had gone up on purpose to Charles T. Harvey at the semi-centennial celebration of the Soo Canal, only from now on *he* could invite everybody to "shake the hand that shook the hand of the man who built the Mackinac Bridge!"

"So I don't fit your previous ideas of what a bridgebuilder should look like?" Dr. Steinman's eyes twinkled behind the glasses as he held up the volume that had been in his lap. "I've been reading this little book about the adventures of Paul Bunyan and Babe the Blue Ox, and it seems that one of their latest adventures was building the Mackinac Bridge."

The man and the boy laughed together in appreciation of the great deeds of the American folklore heroes who, according to the book, had gone on from Mackinac to log off the moon and were currently engaged in felling all the pines on Venus. "I understand some people already are calling it the Paul Bunyan Bridge. No doubt in years to come the legend will relate that Paul Bunyan and his legendary lumberjacks must have built the bridge at Mackinac because ordinary men couldn't possibly have done such an impossible job."

Turning serious on the instant, the famed engineer

put his hands on the boy's shoulders and looked deep
into his eyes. "But men can do anything they set their
hearts on, and make up their minds to do," he said.
"The shortest man on earth can reach the stars. It all
depends on how tall he dreams. Believe me."

"Yes, sir," said the School Reporter. "I believe you."

"What are you going to be?"

"Well, sir, like I told you I'm on the school paper,
but I'm pretty good in math too. I don't know whether
to be an artist or a scientist."

"It's possible to become both," Dr. Steinman advised
in his quiet way, "and the world needs the combination."

Just then the Watchman approached and, after greet-
ings were exchanged, he announced: "Your horseless
buggy's champing at the bit to get back across Long
Mack, son. Can we give you a lift anywhere, Doc?"

Dr. Steinman shook his head. "And please don't tell
anyone where I am," he asked, taking both of them into
his confidence by showing a handwritten sheet of paper
that had been tucked into the little folklore volume.
"I've been working on a poem about bridge-building,"
he admitted, "and I'd appreciate a chance to finish it
alone."

Except for the noise old Tin Liz herself made, it was
a silent ride back across the bridge in the Model T.
Both the Watchman and the School Reporter were busy
with their thoughts.

They arrived at the parking area in Mackinaw City
barely in time for the boy to catch the bus that was to
take him back home. But at the last minute he turned
to take a final look at the Long Crossing. And deep
within himself, so low that nobody else could hear and
make fun of him, he said:

"Someday I'm going to build a bridge like that!"

But, like all the psychic Irish, the Watchman on Mackinac Bridge could hear without being told a word. He slapped the boy on the shoulder and said:

"Sure you will, son, you bet your life you will!"

About the Author

WILLIAM RATIGAN attended the University of Detroit and the University of Chattanooga where he captioned the football team and was an All-Conference quarterback. ' He comes by his enthusiasm for the Inland Seaways and old-fashioned cars through natural inheritance from his father who shipped aboard a Lake Survey boat at the age of twelve,¹ worked his way up to become shakedown cruise engineer for the Ford Eagle Boats during World War One, and founded one of America's oldest continuing automobile dealerships, B. J. Ratigan Motor Sales, Detroit, Michigan.

A fourth generation Detroiter, the author drives a Model T touring car remarkably similar — shamrock doors, hand-pump steamboat whistle, Klaxon horn, and all — to the historic vehicle that plays one of the main characters in the story of *The Long Crossing*.

The author also bears a certain kinship to the school reporter in the book. Six months before the Japanese attack on Pearl Harbor, William Ratigan, because he combined network news experience with basic language training, was placed in charge of NBC's Far Eastern Listening Post, commanding a corps of Chinese, French, Dutch, Japanese, and Russian interpreters. Throughout World War Two he served as Managing News Editor of NBC's Western Division, supervising network commentators and war correspondents in the Pacific Theater of Operations. First to report the Sergeant Grashio account of the "March of Death" on Bataan, he later covered the first UN Conference in San Francisco and was named by *Radio Life* magazine "the best all-around radio newsman in the world."

When V-J Day permitted his return to his native state of Michigan, the author began research on a series of books designed to celebrate the romantic history of America's Inland Seas. Tenth in this series, *The Long Crossing* includes a number of the characters, real and fictional, who already have appeared in *Young Mister Big, Hiawatha* and *America's Mightiest Mile, The Adventures of Captain McCargo, Straits of Mackinac!* and *Soo Canal!*

William Ratigan's stories and serials have appeared in various national magazines, including the *Saturday Evening Post,* and they have been dramatized for radio-T-V presentation. In recognition of his research and writings, he has been appointed Member at Large to the Advisory Council on U. S. Naval Affairs as well as Consultant to the Smithsonian Institution on technical development of Great Lakes craft. Recently at the traditional naming ceremony held each year on the Upper Great Lakes, he was made a Chief of the Algonquin nation of the Ottawa-Chippewa tribes and given the Indian name of Opwa-non iian Kanotong, "Interpreter of Dreams."

An old fish shanty along the Charlevoix waterfront has been converted by the author into his writing workshop. Called the Dockside Press, this quaint establishment has been painted by famous artists and is listed in tourist guides as one of the sights to see on a trip around the Great Lakes. Parked outside on any seasonable day may be seen a Model T touring car that could be mistaken for the twin of "Tin Liz" in *The Long Crossing.*

William Ratigan's
Great Lakes Panorama

Here, told in a series of historical novels and imaginative biographies steadily receiving wider recognition as enduring contributions to our national heritage, is the story of America's fabulous Inland Seaway, the romance and high adventure of our continental oceans and their connecting waters that join Quebec to New Orleans, Buffalo to Chicago, Milwaukee to Duluth, and every port on the Great Lakes to the harbors of the seven seas.

SOO CANAL! — Honored with an unprecedented foreword by General Douglas MacArthur, this colorful historical novel celebrates the American frontier spirit that drew men irresistibly toward a remote Northwest portage a century ago to transform it into an international waterway greater than the Suez and Panama canals combined.

STRAITS OF MACKINAC! — Kaleidoscopic glimpses of history, set in the form of a stream-of-consciousness novel, showing the surge of great-hearted destinies toward the Crossroad of the Great Lakes and the romance of Inland Seaway transportation, from the ghost canoes and phantom sails of the past to the racing yachts and 700-foot ore carriers of the present.

THE ADVENTURES OF CAPTAIN McCARGO — This picaresque novel about a typical Great Lakes sailing master draws an illuminating picture of a lusty young America in the heyday of sail, when flying clouds of canvas bowled rakish hulls across the freshwater seas to carry supplies and settlers to the prairies of Middle America and the wilderness of the North Country.

YOUNG MISTER BIG — Colorful life story of Charles T. Harvey, the young traveling salesman whose pioneer canal and locks opened up a real Northwest Passage into the Lake Superior iron ranges that insured victory for the United States in two world wars.

HIAWATHA AND AMERICA'S MIGHTIEST MILE — This historical essay includes the entire text and notes of Longfellow's national epic, reproduced from one of the rare first edition copies. The book as a whole is an amazing revelation of the interlocking destinies of the Cambridge poet's masterpiece and the Upper Great Lakes region that he never saw.

THE LONG CROSSSING — A dream of great bridges and how that dream came true, up and down the Inland Seaway and around the world, as narrated by an old Lakes captain known simply as the Watchman on Mackinac Bridge.

HIGHWAYS OVER BROAD WATERS — An epic of bridge-building, this major biography of the contemporary figure who stands out as the greatest bridge engineer of all time, David B. Steinman, is global in sweep but quite naturally pays predominant attention to American water crossings, where the world's longest suspension spans have been built, with the crowning example soaring across the Inland Seaway at the Straits of Mackinac.

THE BLUE SNOW*

THE ADVENTURES OF PAUL BUNYAN & BABE**

TINY TIM PINE***

***These three volumes of American folktales, illustrated by Reynold H. Weidenaar, form a trilogy on the Paul Bunyan myth cycle and bring to the public a number of hitherto unrecorded happenings in the giant lumberjack legend.